# POPCORN TO ROCK 'N' ROLL

## S.K. MOORE

Popcorn to Rock 'n' Roll is a fascinating biographical history, written as a novel, surprising, sometimes shocking and often funny.

Reg Calvert is a dreamer, impulsive and determined to succeed. When he falls in love with Dorothy and marries at eighteen he has little thought of the consequences. Too soon he feels trapped by marriage and children. Dorothy wants stability and Reg wants freedom but he needs Dorothy as his anchor. When Reg first hears Bill Haley's 'Rock Around The Clock,' he has a dream.
To bring Rock 'n' Roll to England.

Reg is like the Pied Piper, as young boys, musicians and singers, give up their jobs to follow him as he creates a new way of providing entertainment for teenagers. Behind the scenes, life is exciting but the reality of being a 'star' is far from glamorous!

Dedicated to the memory of two extraordinary people
# REG AND DOROTHY CALVERT

## ACKNOWLEDGEMENTS

My sincere thanks to everyone who has helped with the production
of this book including friends who have proof read: Paula Ball, Geoff
Billington, Maggie Eggar, Sheila Karran, C.J. Moore and Daphne Powis.
My husband Lyndon, for his help and patience.
Most of all, my thanks to the 'boys' for telling me their story.

## CONTRIBUTORS INCLUDE:

Colin Angel, (Colin Wilsher). Buddy Britten, (Geoffrey Glover-Wright).
Tony Burnett, Jeff Chalke. Glen Dale, (Richard Scarforth). Dorothy
Calvert (1928 – 2010). Don Ker. David Jay, (David Hunter). Johnny
Martin, (Martin Upperdine). Roger James, (Roger Scarrott). Terry Scott.
Danny Storm, (David Hurran). Alistair Tritten.
RESEARCH ASSISTANCE FROM: Wikipedia, Pete Chambers and
David St John (www.davidstjohn.co.uk).

**FIRST EDITION**

**ISBN 978-0-9515116-7-1**

**Fillongley Publications CV7 8PB**

# CONTENTS

*Photo (above):* 1946 Reg and Dorothy Calvert on their Wedding Day
*Photo (page 1): Danny Storm with Pete Mist, Colin Angel, Tony Burnett.*

**PHOTOGRAPHS – from the Calvert Collection**
**Other photographs supplied by Johnny Martin** (JM)
Front cover by S.K. Moore www.susan-moore.co.uk

**Produced as a stage play 2009 & 2011**
**Information about the plays and books**
**www.regcalvert-plays.co.uk**

**Book orders email: fillongleypub@btinternet.com**

4

# 1. HUDDERSFIELD BLUES

Huddersfield 1946, was a dismal place at any time of year and throughout the long winter months, fogs and smogs hung low across the valley, shrouding soot grey streets and blackened mills. Or, if the wind blew, away went the fog and in its place, gusts howled up alleys, knocking small children off their feet and forcing folk to walk at odd angles as they fought against the force of the elements. And then the rain would fall, sometimes soft and gentle, washing streets but not the black grime that held fast to buildings. Other times it fell like silver iced daggers that pierced through clothing and drenched the soul.

Reg Calvert, his head and back turned away from the icy north wind, dug with a short handled spade and picked out pieces of black glistening coal with brass tongues. Hastily he stacked, rock upon black rock into the well-polished copper scuttle. He raised his head and happened to glance across to the window opposite. He stopped; transfixed. He forgot the cold and the wind. He forgot the coal in the scuttle. He was staring at the vision of an angel. Light fell from the window to the yard where he stood and it seemed to wrap around the body of a girl and give her a luminescent glow. His eyesight was not good, so he blinked. He looked again, drinking in the vision . She was beautiful. The most beautiful girl he had seen. He shivered, not from cold or the icy wind but with the irrevocable knowledge he had fallen in love, in love with an angel.

Lilia Calvert, silver haired, wise and perceptive, watched Reg gazing across the yard to the window of the doctor's surgery. She had seen the doctor's new secretary, a pretty girl, slim with dark wavy hair and large blue eyes. Her heart went out to this boy. She loved him and he was different from other boys, inventive, gentle and kind. He was special and gave her a reason to keep on living.

"Reggie, could you fetch my new prescription? My tablets are nearly finished."

"Yes Mam, I'll go. I'll be just a minute," replied Reg, his face breaking into a smile. He ran upstairs, two steps at a time and found notepaper and a pen. He sat on his bed and thought, what should he write? A few minutes later he was whistling, *I'm off to see the Wizard, the wonderful Wizard of Oz*. He walked down the street and round the corner to the doctor's surgery. He was an optimist and today he was lucky, the girl was in reception. He confidently passed over the prescription with his own note and smiled hopefully.

Dorothy read the note with disdain. *"Please can I take you to the cinema? I can meet you after work one evening. Reg Calvert."* She glanced at the boy. He was not good looking and his red wavy hair was brylcreemed back from his face. He was not her sort, too cocky and flamboyant. She had seen him before and today he wore a bold blue check suit with matching blue suede shoes. Dorothy pushed the note back and said haughtily as he continued to smile at her. "I'll make up the prescription if you'd like to take a seat."

It was 1946 and the Second World War had just ended. Only the previous year, everyone had held street parties and celebrated the victory. Fathers, brothers and sons who returned from the war with a sense of excitement that life would be better. Instead they trod a road deep with potholes of disappointment. The post war reality was poverty, rationing, unemployment and a massive housing shortage.

Wednesday night was the highlight of the week for those young people who could afford to go to the dance at the Huddersfield Baths. The swimming pool was converted into a ballroom and a crystal ball revolved from the ceiling, showering a thousand sparkling lights on the throng of dancers, as they waltzed and quick stepped to the rhythm of the big bands. This week's star attraction was Joe Loss and his orchestra.

"Mind tha not late back lass," Dorothy's mother called out.

"Okay Mum," replied Dorothy gaily as she braced herself against the icy wind and walked to the bus stop where she met her friend, Maggie.

It was the custom for girls to arrive first and spend time in the cloakroom, adding final touches to make-up and hair, before making their entrance, in anticipation that a tall dark and handsome young man would be waiting for them. In reality, few men were tall, dark or even handsome, but they were smart in their Sunday suits with white shirt and tie or if they were in the forces, they wore military uniform. The young men hung about in small groups, eyeing up the girls who sat around the edge of the hall as they waited to be asked to dance. Dorothy and Maggie found seats near the front and talked while glancing at likely candidates for romance. In the background, a 78-rpm record could barely be heard above the general sound of chatter and laughter as everyone waited for the Big Band to be announced and start playing.

There was a hush in the hall as the stage curtains were pushed aside to make a gap for a young man to step through. He had red wavy hair that was brylcreemed smoothly back. He looked very smart, wearing a black tuxedo, white shirt, black satin bow tie and black leather polished shoes.

"Good Evening, Ladies and Gentlemen. Welcome to Huddersfield Baths."

Dorothy tried to hide her face behind her hand but it was too late, he had seen her. "I don't believe it," she whispered to Maggie.

"Believe what?" asked Maggie, following her gaze.

The compére paused to smile as he caught Dorothy's eye. "Tonight is the night you have been waiting for. Are you In The Mood?" Reg waited for a response from the audience who cheered and whistled at the title of Joe Loss's signature tune. "Are you In The Mood for love?" Reg smiled as he caught Dorothy's eye again. "Tonight is a night of love and romance. Later we'll have competitions, a Spot Dance and some fun. But now we have the fantastic Jo Loss Orchestra. Are you *In The Mood?*" Reg paused as he waited for the reply from the audience. "Are you *In The Mood?*" The crowd, whistled, cheered and clapped in response. "Let's hear it. Lets have a big welcome for the wonderful Joe Loss and his fabulous orchestra."

The curtains swished back as the music commenced to reveal gold shimmering trumpets and saxophones and the polished faces of musicians as they started to play their hit record, "In the Mood."

"Did you see him?" asked Dorothy.

"You mean him?" replied Maggie laughing as she glanced towards a geeky boy.

"No. Not him. The compére. You know. The boy announcing the band, that was him."

Maggie looked up at Reg who made a point of smiling at them as he walked off stage. "That was him was it?"

"You know, the boy I told you about who lives behind the doctor's surgery." Dorothy's cheeks were blushing pink. "I can't believe it. I didn't know he worked here or I wouldn't have come. Do you know what he did last week? He pretended to be ill."

"He might have been ill," replied Maggie.

"He's mad, not ill. The doctor knew straight away so he prescribed sugar tablets to make him better."

Maggie looked quizzical. "If he wasn't ill, why did he give him some sugar tablets?"

Dorothy laughed. "The doctor gives everyone tablets or medicine. Patients expect it."

"Sounds like your doctor is mad. Remind me not to see him when I'm ill," replied Maggie whose attention was distracted.

"Anyway, I made up his prescription, one tablet four times a day after meals and I said, I hoped he would feel well soon. And he said he would only feel well again if I agreed to go on a date with him. But that's not all."

"He's nice," replied Maggie as she made eyes at a tall young man with dark hair who had just entered the hall and joined up with the geeky one.

"I didn't tell you what he did on Monday."

"What do you think of those boys over there?" asked Maggie looking sideways at Dorothy. "They're looking at us. I bags the one with the dark hair. Sorry, what were you saying?"

Dorothy glanced at the young men and continued. "On Monday, he put a loudspeaker outside in his back yard, which is directly behind our surgery."

Maggie repeated in astonishment. "A loudspeaker! "

"Yes. And then he played the piano and sang love songs all morning. I was so embarrassed. And you can't imagine how mad the doctor became. He sent the office manager round to see him and threatened to call the police if he didn't stop."

"He must be mad about you," replied Maggie, making eyes at the boy with the dark hair. "I wouldn't mind a date with him. I wish someone was that crazy about me. If you turned round and smiled, they might come over."

"No need," replied Dorothy. "You're doing enough smiling for both of us. And I really don't fancy the boy wearing glasses. He's not my type."

"You're so particular," replied Maggie huffily. "He looks fine to me."

"Well you can have him and I'll have the one with the dark hair," trumped Dorothy.

"No. I bagged him first. ... Oh hello. They're coming over," whispered Maggie, looking coy.

Dorothy scowled at Maggie as she accepted the invitation to dance.

"I'm Cyril."

"Dorothy."

"I'm pleased to meet you. I'm sorry I'm not good at dancing. My mother's been trying to teach me.

"Ow," squealed Dorothy, protesting as Cyril stepped on her toes for the second time.

"Sorry," replied Cyril, somewhat bashfully. "This is the first time I've asked a girl to dance."

Dorothy decided it would be better to be silent and give the young man no notion she might be interested in him. They continued round the dance floor and as the music faded, she thanked Cyril politely, turned her back and walked to her seat. Maggie remained on the dance floor, triumphant, waiting for the second dance. Dorothy threw her a look of desperation as Cyril followed like a sheepdog. He planted himself on the seat next to Dorothy. How she wished he would go away and leave her on her own. He was going to spoil her evening. Maggie danced and Dorothy sat in silence watching the band. Maggie smiled and laughed while Dorothy inwardly groaned. Cyril was here to stay. She was left with two alternatives. Go home early or stick with him for the rest of the evening.

Reg patrolled the dance floor, observing the audience and the band, making sure the night went with a swing, so numbers for the next week's dance would stay up. He made a point of dancing with girls who seemed to be on their own and as he casually walked by Dorothy, he stopped, held out his hand and asked, "May I have this dance?"

"A pleasure," smiled Dorothy, feeling that Reg was the better option of the two. At least he could dance. "Are you feeling better now?" she asked.

"Much better, now I've seen you again," smiled Reg.

Dorothy's feet floated round the dance floor as Reg led her gracefully in style. "I didn't know you were a compére. I thought you were a hairdresser."

"I'm a hairdresser during the day, but on Wednesday nights, I'm a compére. On Friday and Saturday nights, I sometimes play in a little band with my Dad."

"You keep busy," said Dorothy impressed.

"I like to be busy."

As the song came to an end, Reg escorted Dorothy back to her seat where Cyril was waiting. Reg winked and whispered in her ear. "I'll rescue you again, soon, my damsel in distress."

Dorothy was impressed by Reg's charm and his dancing skills but most of all by the way he ran the dance, organising the crowd into competitions and his easy way of taking control. He had a charisma she had not noticed before in the doctor's surgery.

"May I have this dance?"

Dorothy smiled each time he came over to her. He wasn't her sort, but it was better than sitting the whole evening with Cyril.

"Can I take you home?" asked Reg tentatively.

"No thanks, I'll go home with Maggie."

Reg glanced at Maggie. "It looks like she has a date."

"I can catch the bus, thank you."

"I've got my motorbike outside and I'll drive very slowly. I'll be at the stage door at ten thirty five. It'll be better than waiting for a bus."

Dorothy broke into a smile. "I suppose I might if you drive slowly." And then she thought. "What am I doing? Accepting a lift off him!" "No, really, it's okay. I'll catch the bus before the end. I live the other side of town."

"It's all right. I'd like to take you home."

Dorothy felt trapped into accepting his lift, but he was as good as his word and drove her to her front gate slowly and safely.

"Thank you," Dorothy said as she let go of Reg and carefully climbed off the bike. Her joints were stiff with cold and she felt as though she had turned into a wooden puppet with disjointed movement. "Would you like to come in for a cup of tea and a warm, before you drive back?"

Reg made no reply but balanced his bike by leaning it on the garden fence and followed through the side door. Dorothy put her finger to her lips and said "Shush. Mother will be asleep." Quietly, she lifted the latch and beckoned Reg to follow. As Dorothy switched on the light, she jumped with surprise. Her mother sat at the scrubbed pine kitchen table. The small stout woman with a round face, glared at them through round spectacles. She was wearing a cotton nightdress under a maroon quilted dressing gown and on her head was a brown net covering a mass of small hair rollers.

"Hello Mum, I thought you'd be in bed," said Dorothy startled.

"That's what thought did," retorted her mother in her broad Yorkshire accent. "With that reet din, thou'd awaken tha dead. So who's this tha've brought in off the street?"

Reg stepped forward and held out his hand. "Good evening, you must be Dorothy's mother? I'm right pleased to meet you." He continued to hold his hand out for a moment and then let it fall to his side as it was rebuffed. "I'm Reg Calvert. I live at the back of the doctor's surgery."

"Oh aye, so that's 'im is it?" responded Dorothy's mother, ignoring Reg and looking directly at her daughter in disdain.

Dorothy shifted nervously and turned her back to her mother and smiled at Reg. She fetched cups and filled the kettle with water, lit the gas stove and rested it on the flames. "I'm going to make a cup of tea. Would you like one?"

"Nowt for me," answered her mother sharply as she stood and folded her arms in front of her. "It's late. You've work tomorrow."

"Would you like a cup Reg?" asked Dorothy, making a defiant stand of independence against her domineering mother.

Quickly assessing the situation, Reg replied. "No, it's all right thanks. I'm not really thirsty and I've to get up in the morning. I've some early hair appointments. So I'll be off now. Good night." He glanced towards Dorothy's mother and smiled warmly. "Pleasure to meet you."

Dorothy opened the door, stood by it as she waved goodbye to Reg as he walked away, down the garden path to his bike. Then she turned to face her mother as she shut the door. "You were really rude. You shouldn't speak to people like that."

"And I hope thee won't darken my door by bringing him back again. And al tell thee summat. Nowt good will come of that young man."

Dorothy looked shocked. "What do you mean? You've never seen him before so how can you know?"

"Just what I said, nowt good will come of that young man. He'll come to a sticky end just mark my words young lady. He's no good so don't thee go seeing 'im again."

*Photo:* Ada Calvert (clarinettist). Edward Pearce (violinist).
Lilia Calvert. Newfoundland Dog

# 2. LOVE ON CASTLE HILL

Reg wasted no time. After waiting for months to take Dorothy out, he met her every day from the surgery and walked with her to the bus stop. He was pleasant and kind and treated her like a lady. He took her to the cinema on Monday and the following Sunday, he took her for a ride into the country on his motorbike. Prepared this time, she had wrapped up with warm clothes and a scarf around her head.

"I just love coming up here to Castle Hill," said Dorothy shyly. "You can see Huddersfield down there and all the little people. If I could fly, I would fly away from all of this. The smoke and the smog, the factories and the mills and the little little people with their little minds."

Reg looked surprised at her outburst. "And your family?"

"I'd miss my younger brother, John," replied Dorothy thoughtfully.

Reg parked his motorbike and they walked slowly, side by side, bracing themselves against the fresh northerly wind. Reg had not decided what he should do to stop the agonising pain of desire he felt for Dorothy. He could hardly bear it. They stopped to look at the view and he turned and drew her closer and looked deep into her blue eyes. He gently pushed back strands of long chestnut brown hair that had escaped from her scarf and tried to kiss her, but she quickly moved her head away. They walked on.

"I'm leaving in a few weeks time. I've received my call-up papers." Reg let go of Dorothy's hand and started to march up and down as if he were a soldier and Dorothy giggled. "The war to end all wars is over. And they want me to join the army." He took Dorothy's hand as they started to walk again. "I don't know why the old fogies who run the country don't fight it out between themselves. If they were going to get killed they wouldn't do it. Each country that wants to go to war should have one man represent them and let them fight it out in a boxing ring. Or the old fogies could fight it out between themselves."

"You are funny," said Dorothy. "None of the other boys I know say the things you do."

"I'll be eighteen in two weeks time."

"We're nearly twins" laughed Dorothy. "I'll be eighteen in three week's time."

"I expect they'll send me to Palestine. The lads are calling it suicide corner and I'm not looking forward to it."

"It's exciting to go abroad and you won't go straight away; you'll have to do some training?"

"I'm to be stationed at Catterick near Darlington."

"It's nice there," said Dorothy thoughtfully. "I've been on a coach trip to Darlington and if I remember right, it's a quaint old town with a clock tower right in the centre of a market square."

"It's nicer here, in Huddersfield with you," replied Reg, becoming serious. "Did you know that you've been on my mind every moment of every day since I first saw you last November?"

"Last November?" repeated Dorothy surprised.

"I could see you through the window as you were typing in the doctor's office. The light bulb was behind you and you glowed like an angel. I knew you were for me. But it's taken me four long months to persuade you to have a date. I tried everything to make you notice me."

"I did notice you. I couldn't help it when you came to collect your mother's prescription."

Reg squeezed her warm gloved hand. "She's my grandmother."

"Oh. I wondered why she was so much older," replied Dorothy.

"My grandparents brought me up. My parents are musicians. My father's a violinist but I've never met him. He left before I was born. My mother is brilliant. She plays clarinet and saxophone and has travelled the world and played in most of the women's bands. You should hear her play," said Reg proudly.

"I thought you said you had two sisters and a brother."

"When she married and settled down she had three more children. She kept promising to take me with her," Reg explained with emotion in his voice.

"But you stayed on with your grandparents?"

Reg paused and looked far into the distant hills before he spoke again. "I don't think she wanted me."

14

*Photo:* c1925 (left) Ada Calvert

"That's sad," said Dorothy thoughtfully. "I can't understand a mother not wanting her child."

Reg shrugged his shoulders. "I try to think of her as my sister and call her Ada. My Mam and Dad brought me up, so they're my parents."

"And your Mum is lovely," said Dorothy smiling.

"Yes, she always spoilt me and got between my Dad and me when he wanted to beat me. He used to run after me when I got up to mischief and shout "I'll beat tha livin' daylights out of thee.""

"Did he beat you?"

"Often," replied Reg. "What about your family?"

"My mother hit me when she was angry and sometimes chased me with a stick but I can run faster than she can. She has terrible tempers," giggled Dorothy.

"What about your Dad?"

"He died when I was three. He was my mother's second husband. Her first husband died of diabetes and she really loved him. Then she met my Dad, his first wife had died of consumption and she knew he had two children. On their wedding day, he went and fetched five more from various orphanages."

"You're joking! He didn't tell her before they married?"

15

"No. She had no idea. He was a miner and we lived at Kilner Bank in a small miner's cottage. Before they had me, they had a baby boy who died of meningitis. Then my Dad died of consumption. I don't remember him but all the family said he was a very clever man. Next, my stepbrother, Jack, died of consumption. He was lovely. He bought me my first big doll before he went into the isolation hospital. We went to visit him and I remember waving at him through the window. We weren't allowed to go inside and he didn't come home again." Dorothy paused, with sadness, and they walked on quietly for a while.

"How did your Mum manage?" asked Reg.

"It was hard for her after my Dad died. The eldest two had married but my other stepbrothers and sisters were terrified they were going to be sent back to an orphanage and begged my mother to keep the family together. She agreed and she found work cleaning other people's houses, and the older ones gave her their un-opened wage packets and she gave them pocket money. And then I wasn't well and kept coughing and coughing. The doctor told my mother he thought I would get consumption. My mother did her best to feed me up and keep me well but the cough got worse and worse. The doctor was good and he wrote to Huddersfield Council and persuaded them give us a new council house at Almondbury."

"It must have been reet tough for your Mum."

"It was. But we never went hungry or without."

"And your younger brother, John?" queried Reg.

"John. Yes. He's five years younger than me. My step brother Jim is only a few years younger than my mother and …."

"I see," said Reg, with understanding.

"We both have skeleton's in our family cupboard," commented Dorothy. "Because of the law, she couldn't marry Jim and I think the shame of it made her bitter. Before our John came along, I remember it being a happy home with lots of laughter."

"And Jim still lives with your Mum," asked Reg.

"Yes, but they have separate bedrooms. Our Jim's been good to me. When I passed the eleven plus with high marks, I was offered a place at Greenhead High School."

"That snobby school," laughed Reg.

"Jim persuaded my Mum to let me go. She was dead against it as it was going to cost too much to buy the school uniform, books and hockey stick. He helped to pay for everything. Our Jim's clever too. He passed the exams but my Dad was too poor to pay for him and he's always said that if they had let him go to grammar school he wouldn't be working down the mine. He wanted me to have a chance."

"I didn't pass any exams," admitted Reg. "My reading and writing isn't good and my spelling is awful. I could always understand things but I couldn't write it down."

"That's odd," said Dorothy.

"I love science and the science teacher let me take the class as he said I knew more about it than he did. Then one day, one of the experiments went wrong and there was a big explosion," laughed Reg.

"Oops," laughed Dorothy.

"You'll have to meet my parents properly. My Dad works as an engineer. I expect he'll take you down to the cellar."

"What's in the cellar?"

"Something big," laughed Reg. "An enormous contraption! He's trying to invent a machine that works on the earth's centrifugal force so you can have perpetual motion. He's been working on it all his life and I sometimes go down and help him. It's really interesting. He's got some fantastic tools and he's good at making things."

"Gosh," said Dorothy. "My mother wants me to go to university and train to become a doctor."

"Is that what you want to do?"

"I'm not sure. It would cost a lot of money and I don't think it would be fair on my mother to keep on supporting me. It was hard enough for her to pay for me to go to the high school and I like working in the doctor's surgery. I've learnt how to make prescriptions and it's good experience."

"Have you thought about the future?" asked Reg.

"Not really, only that I want to leave Huddersfield and go south."

"One day, I'd like my own business. To work for myself and not have other people telling me what to do," said Reg. "And I'd buy a big house in the country and have a big limousine car."

"Oh yes," laughed Dorothy. "And pigs can fly."

"If you dream something, you can make it happen," said Reg.

"I believe in fate," said Dorothy. "If it's fate, it will happen and there's nothing you can do about it."

"I believe in making things happen," replied Reg. "Although it was fate I happened to see you in the doctor's surgery. Before I met you, I thought I'd like to stay a bachelor until I'm really old. At least thirty."

"And I'd like to stay an old maid, until I am at least twenty-five," agreed Dorothy.

Reg stopped walking and wrapped his arms around Dorothy and held her close. He took her face in his gloved hands and kissed her gently on the lips. As they pulled apart she looked around, aware there were other walkers who could be watching them. There was no one, and once more, they walked, not saying anything. After a few minutes silence, Reg started to speak, very slowly.

"Did you know... I've fallen in love with you?"

Dorothy looked at the ground beneath her feet and felt an electric pulse rush through her being. "You love me?"

Reg replied confidently. "Yes I do. I've loved you since the first moment I saw you." And then he called out loudly to the sky. "I love you, I love you, I love you."

Embarrassed by Reg's outburst, she began to giggle. "Shush, someone will hear you."

Reg smiled and swung his arms out and spun round and round. "I don't care, let them hear me, I want everyone to know. I love you, I love you, I love you."

"Shush," giggled Dorothy.

Reg stopped and they continued to walk as Reg spoke hesitantly. "I dream about you every night and I know you're the person for me. And I know that together we can go anywhere. Fly to the moon. Be anything. Do anything. I know we can. I love you."

"I don't want the moon," replied Dorothy thoughtfully. "I'm happy with my feet on the ground. All I want is to move south."

Reg smiled and they stopped walking as he turned to face her. "You can. We can. I've thought about you so much. I don't want to wait until I'm thirty anymore. I want you to be my wife." Dropping down and bending on one knee, he looked up and asked, "Will you marry me?"

Dorothy laughed shyly and pulled him up. "You'll get wet knees."

"Will you? Will you marry me?" asked Reg.

"But you don't know me. We've only been going out for one week and we're too young," replied Dorothy, trying to think of reasons why she should say no.

Reg pulled her close and she could feel the warmth of his body. "One week, seven days, one year, seven years." And then he stopped and said quietly. "What does it matter? I know you're the person for me. Will you marry me?"

For a moment, Dorothy hesitated and Reg held his breath.

"I can't imagine being a Mrs."

"So you will? You will marry me?"

"I suppose. I suppose I will."

Reg, in his joy, picked her up off her feet and swung her round and round and Dorothy screamed and laughed. "Put me down, put me down!"

"I'm so happy," said Reg putting her feet gently down. "One day we'll have a big house in the country."

"One day," smiled Dorothy.

"One day soon. Let's get married next week," said Reg as he kissed her passionately.

Dorothy pulled herself away and tried to be sensible. "No, that's too soon. We can wait two years, until you finish in the army and save some money."

"Why wait, when we both know what we want? We can start our lives together. One big adventure."

"Not next week,' replied Dorothy. "It's much too soon."

"What about June? We can have a June wedding," suggested Reg.

"June. Oh Dear. I've just remembered something," said Dorothy seriously.

"Something important?" asked Reg.

"Yes. My mother."

*Photo:* Sarah Jane Rowe

19

# 3. LOVE AND MARRIAGE

If you had put a light to a box of fireworks you would not have seen more sparks than the day Dorothy plucked up courage to break the news to her mother. She shouted, ranted and raged. Dorothy was used to her mother's mood swings and bad temper but this was far worse. As each day passed, instead of accepting the situation, her mother became more angry and abusive.

"We're engaged and I'm going to marry him," insisted Dorothy stubbornly.

"Oh aye. You'll do as the eckers like. Ee hasn't even bought thee a ring," shouted Sarah Jane as she took a swipe at Dorothy, hitting her round the face.

Dorothy's large blue eyes filled with tears. It was no use. The more her mother ranted and raged, the more Dorothy was determined. The door opened and Jim entered.

"What's all this ere shoutin' about our Sarah?"

Sarah Jane looked flushed and a little mad. Dorothy glanced pleadingly at her step- brother as she swished out of the room and stamped upstairs.

"Calm down our Sarah," said Jim, taking a seat at the kitchen table. "Tha lass is head strong wi' a mind of her own. There's nowt thee can say t' change 'er mind once it's made up."

"She wants t" wed "im an" I keep telling "er she's wasted on "im. Ee's no good. But she'll nay listen."

Jim spoke quietly and tried to make the peace, but Sarah Jane was inconsolable.

In the morning, Dorothy packed her bags and left without a word, taking her few belongings. She planned to stay with Maggie for a few days but when Reg met her after work, she broke down in tears.

"You can come and stay at our house," offered Reg. "I'm sure my Mam and Dad won't mind. You can have my room and I'll be away at Catterick most of the time. When I come home, I'll sleep on the settee."

Tom and Lilia welcomed Dorothy into their home as their prospective daughter in law. Lilia was kind and gentle and Tom, a lady's man and raconteur, spoiled Dorothy and kept her entertained with his stories, but she could see through him for what he was and felt sorry for Lilia. The house was modest and could have been more comfortable, except for Tom, who spent all his spare money on tools and equipment to build his invention. Dorothy was interested in science and often went down to the cellar to see what he was doing.

"Why don't you make a smaller model?" suggested Dorothy.

"Nay lass, I need it t' be big."

"The principle would be the same whether it was big or small," replied Dorothy bravely. "And it wouldn't cost so much to build."

Tom looked at her with respect but she realised he would not change his ways. He had spent too many years building big to change course now.

Between the kitchen and the living room lay a dead dog, skinned with its head still attached. Dorothy often looked at it and thought it a strange thing to have on the floor.

"Our Tom used to breed Newfoundland Dogs," explained Lilia. "They were almost extinct and he bred them back again. That was Black Prince, his favourite. When he died, he had him skinned as a rug but we don't walk on him."

Sunday evenings were music night and Dorothy was delighted as the house filled with local musicians. Tom on saxophone, Lilia on piano, a neighbour played violin and anyone else who was there was welcome to join their small band. Over the weeks, Lilia explained about her family of Fosters, Blamires and Hartleys. "We've a few musicians in the family. Tom owned the first saxophone in Yorkshire and taught our Ada to play clarinet and saxophone. And our William is head of music at Dundee College and has a Stradivarius violin. You may have heard his son, Fred Hartley on the radio?"

Dorothy nodded.

"During the war," continued Lilia, "Fred had a sextet and did a lot of broadcasting. He went to Australia and became involved with music programming on the Australian Broadcasting Service. I don't expect we'll see him again."

When Sarah Jane realised her daughter was not returning home, she became more resentful and angry and it became impossible for mother and daughter to communicate. Dorothy stayed away and wrote to her mother saying she wanted consent to marry in June. Sarah Jane refused but Jim persuaded her, pointing out it would be easy to cross the border to Scotland where they could marry with no consent.

Clothes were still rationed after the war and Dorothy saved her clothing coupons and bought a turquoise suit for her wedding outfit and Reg wore his army uniform. The ceremony, quiet and simple, in a little Methodist Chapel, was not as Reg or Dorothy had wished as no one came from either family, except for Jim, who gave Dorothy away. Afterwards they returned to Reg's home for their honeymoon, a week on their own in the house as Tom and Lilia thoughtfully booked a holiday to coincide with the wedding. Reg bought Dorothy a narrow twenty-two carat gold wedding ring and she wore it with pride. She was now a 'Mrs' and it was custom for married women to be called 'Mrs' as a mark of respect, and except for close family and friends, no one ever called her Dorothy again.

After the honeymoon, Reg returned to Catterick and Lilia sat Dorothy down with a cup of tea.

"Have a look at this lass," said Lilia, opening a sideboard drawer and taking out a package wrapped in faded tissue paper. Dorothy unwrapped the paper and inside she saw what looked like a rubber saucer.

"Do thee know what it is?" asked Lilia.

"No," replied Dorothy, shaking her head. Being married and becoming a 'Mrs' was a revelation to Dorothy and she knew nothing about sex.

"It's a cap to stop thee becoming pregnant. I've gone through the change and I'm too old t' have more bairns. You insert the cap into your .... and leave it there just before .... you know what. Afterwards, take it out and douche thee self inside with soap and some of this boric acid powder diluted in water," explained Lilia, passing Dorothy a jar with some powder inside. "Unless thee want t' have bairns now?"

"No, no I don't," replied Dorothy shyly. "We don't want children for a long time. Thank you. I'll try it."

"And if thee need a rest from …. it, just leave a bit of the powder inside and it'll make him sore and he won't want to have it for a while. It'll give thee a break," continued Lilia, much to Dorothy's embarrassment.

When Reg returned home on forty-eight hours leave, Dorothy related the story and they couldn't stop laughing and the rubber cap was never worn. Reg had his own device, a thick rubber condom that he washed out after use ready for the next time. He didn't like to wear it as he didn't get much sensation and Dorothy was forever reminding him what would happen if he didn't. She was surprised that the gentle boy, who had patiently courted her these past few months, was now a passionate and demanding lover.

"We're married and it's legal and you're mine," laughed Reg as he chased her round the bedroom. "Come here. I love you, I love you, I love you."

"Shush," whispered Dorothy. "Your Mam and Dad will hear us."

Afterwards, they lay together, curled up, content and sleepy.

"I was sent to Cirencester last week," said Reg yawning.

"Yes, you said you were going to train as a clerk. Was Cirencester nice?"

"Lovely, very pretty but the course was so boring. I had to write everything down in a book and keep records. I was never good at writing and I kept getting my accounts wrong because I couldn't see the small print clearly. They thought I was kidding so they sent me to Oxford to have my eyes tested."

"What was Oxford like?" asked Dorothy.

"I didn't see much of it, lots of old buildings and university students on bicycles. Do you want the bad news or the good news first?"

"You didn't tell me there was bad news. Just tell me," replied Dorothy yawning.

"The good news is that they won't be sending me out to Palestine or anywhere else to fight."

"That's good," said Dorothy snuggling down.

"And I'm going to be the Camp Barber at Catterick."

"That's wonderful. So what's your bad news?"

"My eyes." Reg paused with the seriousness of the diagnosis. "I've got diseased corneas. A cataract in my right eye which is why it's blurry and the start of one in my left eye."

"Oh no," said Dorothy, shocked, sitting up. "Can they do anything about it?"

"No. Nothing. I'll go blind. Hopefully, I can manage with my left eye until that one goes. It could be twenty years or more before I go blind."

"I suppose so," agreed Dorothy thoughtfully while a vision of the future came into her mind as she tried to imagine what life would be like, married to a blind man. "And they can't do anything?"

"No," replied Reg seriously. "I've decided it's no good thinking too far ahead into the future. Who knows what's going to happen tomorrow or even next week. We have to live for the moment. But on the bright side, I'd rather have bad eyes than go to Palestine and be killed."

"I suppose."

"And the other bit of good news is. I'm staying in Catterick and you can come and live with me."

"I suppose I could," replied Dorothy, snuggling down again. "We could rent a house."

"I've asked around and houses are too expensive. One of the lads is moving out of a farmhouse and we can have his room."

"A room, not a house?"

"Houses are more than my wages and the farmhouse is not cheap. One pound ten shillings a week."

"That's all your wages," said Dorothy dismayed.

"I've an idea. I can start a little dance in a village hall and earn some extra money."

"It would help until I find a job," said Dorothy.

"Guess what? The Army Major needs a secretary. I told him you were very good," said Reg, kissing her neck passionately. "I would be able to see you every day."

Two week's later, Dorothy caught a bus to Catterick and Reg met her in the town and drove her out to an idyllic cream painted farmhouse on the outskirts of Darlington, near the River Skerne.

"They said if you stand perfectly still you'll see kingfishers by the riverbank. And when the weather's warm, we'll be able to swim in the river," said Reg.

"Not me, I can't swim," laughed Dorothy. "I sink and go straight down."

They knocked the big brass door-knocker and could hear inside the yapping of little dogs. Peggy, a young woman of thirty opened the door and shooed the dogs into the kitchen.

"Come in, I'll show thee t' tha room. I expect you're chilled through lass. It'll be reet parky sitting on the back of a motorbike. Don't mind tha dogs, I breed Pekinese and they won't hurt thee. I'll put the kettle on for some tea so come you down t' tha kitchen when thou've settled in. The lavvy's outside in the little shed and I've cut newspaper into squares and put it on a hook behind tha door."

The lodger's bedroom was clean, spacious and simply furnished with an old double bed with black wrought iron posts, a large mahogany wardrobe, bedside cupboard and one easy chair.

"Our first home," said Reg closing the door as Peggy left. "Come here. Oh, how I've missed you."

"Not now," laughed Dorothy, pushing him away. "She'll hear. Wait 'til later."

"I can't wait to get my trousers off," said Reg, unbuttoning his trousers and pulling them down.

"Reg. No! Not now!"

"I itch all over. They won't let recruits wear underpants and I'm coming up with spots," said Reg bending down and pointing his posterior towards her.

"What a sight, lots of blackheads," giggled Dorothy, taking a closer look. "Do you want me to squeeze them?"

"No," said Reg turning round and kissing her.

"Not now," said Dorothy pulling away. "Put your trousers back on."

"The army is stuffed full of stupid rules and regulations," replied Reg cheerfully.

"I'll wash your trousers and see if they soften."

"Just so long as they don't shrink," said Reg kissing her again,

Dorothy started work as secretary to the Army Major and most nights, Reg was allowed to return home to their room in the farmhouse. Reg disliked the discipline of army life, being told what to do and what not to do. He organised a weekly dance and the Army Major commanded Reg to stop, recruits were not permitted to have other employment. Reg agreed of course, but continued to run the dance with Dorothy as the person in charge. Some evenings, he played saxophone in the Army Wing Band with Johnny Dankworth, a superb clarinettist who had studied music at the Royal Academy. They became friends and Dorothy often went to watch them perform. Married life was good and Reg and Dorothy enjoyed being together. They had made the break from their families and started married life as one big adventure, on their own.

After they had been married eighteen months, Dorothy nervously waited for Reg to return home. "I've some news," said Dorothy quietly as she handed Reg an arrowroot biscuit.

"What news?" asked Reg putting his arms around her.

"You know I haven't felt well. The Doctor said I should get better in about five months time. He said I should take it easy. Put my feet up more."

Reg looked quizzical. "That long?"

"Afraid so, five months," smiled Dorothy. "You're going to be a father."

Reg sat for a moment absorbing her words. "Me a Dad? You're pregnant? You're not ill? You're pregnant. I can't take it in, I'm going to be a Dad," grinned Reg.

"Yes, and I'm going to be a Mum."

"When?"

"July. The exact date as my mother's birthday."

"Are you going to tell her?" asked Reg.

"Of course."

"But you haven't spoken to her since we got married."

"She'll want to know she's going to be a grandmother," replied Dorothy thoughtfully. "I can't imagine what she'll say. And I was thinking, we'll need somewhere to stay. We can't stay living in one room. Do you think we'll have enough money to rent a house?"

"I've an idea," replied Reg grinning mischievously and giving Dorothy a hug. "Leave it with me."

# 4. LOVE IN A BUS

Reg whistled happily as he ran up the stairs and burst into the bedroom. "Hi Doe Doe. I've missed you today."

"I didn't hear the bike," said Dorothy surprised as he kissed her.

"No, I didn't bring it," replied Reg grinning. "Let me feel our baby. Has he been kicking today?"

"All afternoon, it's quite embarrassing when I'm sitting down and typing, but the Major doesn't seem to mind. He said I can work right up to the time I have the baby if I want to."

"That's good," said Reg.

"I'm so big now, I look like the side of a bus."

"You look beautiful to me," said Reg as he put his arms around her. "I've a surprise for you. Come and see. It's outside."

"You're up to no good. I can tell with that silly grin on your face," said Dorothy, laughing as he took her hand and started to tug her out of the room.

Just before they reached the back door, Reg stopped. "Close your eyes and keep them closed. No peeping."

"What have you bought? You shouldn't spend your money. We need to save for a house."

"Come on Doe Doe, keep your eyes closed. Now open them."

Dorothy blinked and gasped in dismay. "You've bought an old bus. Why?"

"It was only a few pounds."

"What are we going to do with an old bus?" asked Dorothy irritably.

"I thought we could make some money taking people on trips to the seaside. You could learn to drive so we could take it in turns," grinned Reg.

"No Reg," said Dorothy biting her lip. "We needed that money for a deposit on a house."

"Why pay rent when we can live in an old bus?" said Reg laughing. He loved to tease, make her angry and then calm her down with a kiss.

"Pardon me. You won't get me living in an old bus."

"Don't get mardy. Come in and see our new home," said Reg pulling her up the steps and into the bus. "I'll take the engine out

27

and we can have the bedroom here. A lounge here and the kitchen area here."

"What about a toilet?"

"We can get one of those camping bucket things. It'll be no worse than going down to the lavvy at the bottom of the garden or a pot under the bed."

"I suppose," said Dorothy, gradually coming round to the idea.

"I'll make it very cosy, and I'll get lads from the camp to help."

Dorothy began to look again at the space. "I suppose it would make a home."

"And we won't have to pay rent. No neighbours. No renting rooms in other people's houses," said Reg happily.

Dorothy began to smile. "I suppose I can make curtains to put at the windows."

"And when I'm de-mobbed we can go anywhere you want." said Reg.

"South, as far south as we can travel," laughed Dorothy.

When the weather was mild, they lived like gypsies and slept in the bus. There was a constant party atmosphere as people from the army camp came to help along with a few German prisoners of war who had not returned to their homeland. Dorothy made large pans of stew over a gas ring and fed everyone who came. Reg scrounged materials and salvaged others. Within a few weeks, the bus was beginning to look a caravan.

Peggy kindly offered to let Dorothy have her baby in the room and everything was arranged with the midwife. Being pregnant was uncomfortable. As a girl, Dorothy had injured her back jumping over a 'horse' in the school gym and the pressure of the baby was giving her severe pain.

"I wish it would come early," complained Dorothy. "I can't get comfortable."

"Three weeks to go, not long," replied Reg as he rubbed her back to ease the pain.

"My mother replied today," said Dorothy smiling.

"I thought she would."

"I'll read it to you," said Dorothy, picking up the envelope and taking out the note. *"Dear Dorothy, please come home to have your*

28

*baby. I have prepared your room and borrowed a cot and other baby things. Let bygones be bygones, love Mother."*

"Are you going?"

"I don't know what to do? Everything's been arranged here. But I think I might be better being looked after at home."

"You mean, you don't think I'd look after you," laughed Reg.

"You don't exactly know about babies," smiled Dorothy.

Dorothy realised how hard it was for her mother to swallow her pride and write. With relief, she replied and accepted. Sarah Jane made no mention of Reg but was polite and held her tongue when he came to visit. The baby arrived, late, with a mop of red hair and blue eyes.

"The bairn looks just like her father," said Sarah Jane, cradling her first grandchild.

"I think we'll call her Susan," said Dorothy.

"Why Susan?" asked Reg.

"I've had the same dream for three nights running. We should call her Susan."

"You should always follow your dream," agreed Reg.

Dorothy stayed three weeks with her mother and the rift between them slowly healed. When it was time to leave, Sarah Jane tried to persuade Dorothy to stay longer.

"Nay lass, thee can't live in an old bus with a bairn."

"It's a caravan and very comfortable. You don't need to worry. When Reg is demobbed from the army, we're going to move it south and you can come and visit us."

"South!" exclaimed Sarah Jane in horror. "Tha dun't know what'll happen to thee so far from home."

"I've always wanted to move south and that's where we're going. Reg has been offered a job at a hairdressers in Southampton and he's arranged to transport it down there."

"Eee lass. You've ne'er been south of Leeds. Howd' thee know what it'll be like?"

"It'll be fine," smiled Dorothy happily. And I'm going to stay with his Mam and Dad for a week before we go."

"Tha allus were a stubborn one," replied Sarah Jane, turning away so Dorothy did not see the tears filling her eyes. The thought of losing her daughter again was too much and she walked briskly from the room.

Lilia and Tom spoiled Dorothy and their new great-granddaughter and tried to persuade Dorothy to stay to no avail. Reg came to collect Dorothy and his baby daughter and take them back to the caravan in the side-car he had fitted to his motorbike. Just before they left, Tom thrust a ten-pound note in Dorothy's hand when Reg wasn't looking.

"It'll tide thee over for a rainy day," he whispered. It was unexpected and Dorothy accepted it gratefully.

Arrangements were made to move the caravan south but when they arrived, they were disappointed as they drove from one registered site to another. No one had space for the 'caravan.' In the evening they parked in a quiet lane for the night. Early next morning, there was a knock on the door.

"Good morning," said a man, smiling at them warmly.

"Good morning," replied Reg as he opened the door and returned the smile.

"I live over there in that cottage," pointed the man. "We wondered if you were all right?"

"We just stopped for the night. We're trying to find somewhere to put our caravan. We drove round all day yesterday and all the sites are full."

"Are you from the north?" asked the man.

"Yes, Huddersfield," replied Reg, surprised the man had recognised his accent from the few words he had spoken. Both he and Dorothy tried to speak in the 'King's English' they heard on the radio, and not with the Yorkshire accent or dialect of their parents. "I've been offered a job in Southampton as a hairdresser," explained Reg. "I've to start work tomorrow."

Dorothy came and stood on the step, holding her baby, and smiled at the man.

"You can stay here, in my apple orchard," offered the man. "There's running water from a tap over there and you can connect up with electricity from the house."

Dorothy smiled at the man, thankfully. "Where are we?"

"Hedge End, not so far from Southampton, Fareham or Eastleigh. You can catch a bus to town quite easily."

"Hedge End," repeated Dorothy. It sounded nice.

A small monthly rent was agreed and within a few hours the caravan was pulled into place with the aid of a few more curious cottagers who helped them set up camp in the orchard. It was idyllic. They had found a little bit of heaven.

The following day, Reg drove into Southampton to meet his new employer. He returned home late, looking forlorn and dejected.

"What's the matter?" Dorothy asked as soon as she saw him.

"He's taken someone else on. He promised me the job but he broke his word and now we've nothing. I drove round every hairdressers I could find," said Reg, his voice trailing off. "But no one had a vacancy."

"Oh," said Dorothy, concerned. "You need to find work."

"If I can't do hairdressing I don't know what to do," said Reg slumping in the chair.

"You hold Susie. I'll go across to the cottages and see if they've a newspaper with job vacancies," said Dorothy, removing her apron and putting on some shoes.

Reg applied for every vacancy in vain and joined queues with other unemployed men, only to be turned away. Each evening he came home despondent. "Is this all we've to eat?" asked Reg. "Bread and jam."

"We've little money to buy anything else. There's a small piece of cheese left if you would like it?" replied Dorothy unhappily. She was trying to make the ten pounds last and only buy essentials. The future looked bleak if Reg could not find work.

In the morning, Dorothy opened the caravan door to let the sunlight in and on the doorstep were six eggs, a home-grown lettuce, tomatoes and some new potatoes. She picked up the food and laid them on the kitchen table, smiling.

"The cottagers must have guessed," said Reg, putting his arm around Dorothy.

Reg found various odd jobs but after a short time, would return, dejected. One job lifting and carrying boxes from the back of trucks and loading them into a warehouse, he kept for three weeks before returning home early.

"What ever's the matter? Are you unwell?" enquired Dorothy.

"Leave me alone will you," replied Reg sharply. "I don't need you to nag me."

"Nag you, I was only asking if you were all right?"

"I'm fine. So just leave me alone."

"Play Daddy, play," said Susan toddling up to her father.

"Go away Susie. I'm not in the mood."

Dorothy said nothing more and picked Susan up to stop her crying and sat out on the front step, bouncing her up and down on her knee.

"All you ever do is see to her. You've no time to spend with me any more," said Reg jealously.

"I can't just ignore Susie because you've come home. Now tell me why you're not at work?"

"If you must know, I got the sack."

"The sack," repeated Dorothy.

"Yes, the sack. They don't want me anymore."

"You've never had the sack before."

"They're stupid. They pay peanuts and employ monkeys."

"What did you do?"

"I built a track."

"A track? What sort of track?"

"Like tracks they have in the car industry. It moves one thing to the next thing. I got it working so it moved boxes from the lorries directly into the warehouse without anyone having to carry them. It was brilliant. It would have made life much easier for everyone."

"I suppose it would," said Dorothy.

"All the men went on strike as soon as I got it to work. They thought they would lose their jobs so I got the sack. The gaffer paid me off and said he was very sorry."

Reg became a drifter never staying more than a few weeks with one employer before getting bored. He then spent days of idleness, irritable and deep in thought. Dorothy had difficulty breaking down the barrier between them and tried to motivate him to apply for more work. Eventually he found employment as a ladies hairdresser and also some evening work, playing piano in a club two nights a week.

In the spring, apple blossom scented the air and there was a gentle hum of insects and bees going about their business of pollinating. When the wind blew, tall grasses and wild flowers intermingled and rippled like waves on the sea. Dorothy spent much of her time outdoors, sometimes walking the lanes, proudly pushing Susan in her Silver Cross coach built pram, and other times, enjoying the orchard, watching the wild birds as they flew down to a bird table.

"You ought to get a lawn mower," suggested Dorothy. "Sometimes I lose Susan in the tall grasses."

"Could do," replied Reg, with a lack of enthusiasm.

A few days later, Reg returned from work, whistling merrily. "Come and see what I've got in the side-car. I've been given it to keep the grass short."

"A lawn mower," smiled Dorothy optimistically.

"Not a lawn mower, guess again?"

"A scythe?" laughed Dorothy.

"Nope," replied Reg as he kissed Dorothy and picked Susan up and lifted her to his shoulders. "Let's go and see what Daddy has got to keep the grass short, shall we?" Susan giggled as he bumped her up and down. "Close your eyes," he said to Dorothy. "And no peeping while I open the top."

From inside the sidecar was the sound of bleating. Dorothy blinked in astonishment.

"You've bought a lamb."

"No. It's a baby kid. I was given it."

"A kid goat?" exclaimed Dorothy as she stared in surprise at the tiny black and white creature that jumped about with delight at having been freed from the sidecar. "He's beautiful."

"What shall we call him?" asked Reg.

"Billy the Kid, of course," laughed Dorothy.

"Of course, why didn't I think of that? He likes Susie and he's licking her hand. She seems to have a way with animals, just like her mother."

"I had a letter today from my Mother. Do you want to read it?"

"No, you tell me what she says."

*Photo:* Dorothy and Susan with Billy the Kid in the
apple orchard with caravan (bus) behind.

"It's our John. He's in real trouble," said Dorothy. "He got a girl pregnant."

"You're joking. He's only sixteen," replied Reg chuckling.

"Seventeen" corrected Dorothy. "The baby's called Susan and a year old. Mother has just found out and she's furious. John told no one. He hasn't paid maintenance and the baby has nothing. No cot, no clothes or anything. The girl's parents are totally against her. They say she's brought shame to their family."

"So. What's John going to do about it?" asked Reg.

"Mother has told him he has to do the honourable thing and marry the girl whether he likes it or not."

"Oops," laughed Reg.

"It's not a laughing matter," said Dorothy.

"I expect your Mum will make him have a shotgun wedding."

"It's not right to get a girl pregnant and not take responsibility for your action," retorted Dorothy. "Some men think they can have their way and the baby is nothing to do with them and most girls are forced to give their baby away for adoption."

"That's life. Always was, always will be," replied Reg, more seriously.

The seasons came and went and they were happy. When Reg was in work, he gave Dorothy his unopened wage packet for her to budget for the week and he kept any extra money he earned in tips or playing piano.

"Here's my wages packet," said Reg, handing the small brown envelope to Dorothy.

"And where's the tips?" asked Dorothy, knowing in advance he had kept them.

Photo: Reg playing with Susan on caravan steps.

"What tips?" asked Reg grinning. It was a game they played each week that Dorothy rarely won.

"I was sick this morning," mentioned Dorothy. "But I feel a lot better now."

"Daddy, Daddy, play with me." interrupted Susan.

"Okay. We'll play ball outside with Billy the Kid. Let's see if he's good at heading balls."

Dorothy smiled as she watched Reg kick a ball to Susan, who kept tumbling over and giggling in the long grass.

"Tea's ready," called Dorothy.

"What've we got?" asked Reg, picking Susan up and carrying her into the caravan.

"Can you wash her hands first under the tap," called Dorothy.

"Something smells good," said Reg.

"I managed to buy a tin of tuna fish and I've made a hot cheese sauce."

"Mmm, very nice. Goes well with mashed potatoes," approved Reg. "Makes a change from stew or corned beef hash."

"I've bought you something," said Reg, grinning like a Cheshire cat. I'll fetch it from the side-car." Reg returned a few minutes later and placed a large brown paper sack on the table.

"Corn. Why have you bought corn?" asked Dorothy in surprise as she peered inside the sack. "Are you planning to keep chickens?"

35

"Cluck, Cluck Cluck. No chickens. It's not any old corn, it's popping corn," said Reg continuing to grin.

"Popping corn?" queried Dorothy.

"Yep. I thought I'd have a go at making popcorn and sell it at the fairgrounds and markets to earn a bit of extra money. I'll never earn much as a hairdresser and we could do with a bit more cash."

"Popcorn. Do you think you'll be able to sell it?"

"Don't see why not. And maybe I'll make toffee apples if I can get enough sugar or glucose syrup," said Reg.

"It could work, I suppose," replied Dorothy.

"I can make popcorn in your stew pan. We could do two markets if I dropped you off first. We could earn twice as much."

"What me? Working on a market?" said Dorothy in surprise.

"Why not? All you have to do is call out, Popcorn and Toffee Apples For Sale."

"No, no way, I don't want to work on a market."

"Since the end of the war to end all wars there are no decent jobs. If I didn't get tips, the wage they pay me would hardly be worth going in for. What future is there in working for other people?" asked Reg.

When Susan had settled down and gone to sleep, Dorothy decided to break her news. "You know I was sick this morning? Feel here." Dorothy placed his hand on her stomach.

"Not again," said Reg irritably.

"It's your fault, you insisted on having your way. You won't wear that condom."

"You'll have to get rid of it," replied Reg.

"Don't be ridiculous," retorted Dorothy.

"I'll buy a bottle of gin. Put the boiler on and I'll fetch water from the pump. And then you can sit in a hot bath," said Reg putting on his jacket.

"No Reg," said Dorothy, grabbing his jacket sleeve. "I'm not going through that again, I told you last time when you got me drunk. It was horrible and I was sick. It's good to have two children close together."

"One's more than enough for me."

"You'll have to think about the consequences of what you're doing next time," said Dorothy quietly, turning her back on him and trying not to cry.

36

"I'll go and get the gin."

"No Reg, I've told you, I'm not going through that again."

"I didn't plan to get married and have two children by the time I was twenty-two."

"Nor did I," shouted Dorothy before she could stop herself.

"I don't want another baby," said Reg quietly. "I do not want another baby."

"It's your fault," shouted Dorothy. Her temper was quick and fiery like her mother's whereas Reg was quiet when he was angry. "I told you at the time but you wouldn't listen. You've to take responsibility for your actions."

Reg stood up and automatically hit out at her with his hand and slapped her around the face. The force knocked her to the floor. Dorothy screamed in shock and pain. For a moment she said nothing. Reg stared at her coldly.

"You should think what you do," hissed Dorothy. "If you ever hit me again, I'll call the police. You've no right to hit me. I'm your wife and I won't have you hit me like other men do. I won't stand for it."

Reg made no apology. He looked dejected and miserable. Susan was now wide awake, standing in her cot and screaming. "You can be quiet too," said Reg irritably as he slumped back into the easy chair. He felt trapped with nowhere to go.

When the atmosphere had calmed and Susan had gone back to sleep, Dorothy spoke quietly, with understanding. "You have to be more careful or I'll end up like my Irish grandmother. She had thirteen children," warned Dorothy.

"I didn't plan to have children and I don't want this one," replied Reg sullenly. "You'll have to take the gin."

"I won't," replied Dorothy quietly. "So don't waste money buying some."

"It's your fault," said Reg.

"Everything's my fault," answered Dorothy.

"If you weren't so beautiful I wouldn't want you."

"Then you'll have to be more careful," replied Dorothy as she put the dishes from their meal into a bucket, ready to wash under the tap in the morning. "This isn't much fun for me either," she said.

"I didn't want children or to live in an old bus. But I'm trying to make the best of things as they happen."

*Photo:* Reg and the popcorn stand

# 5. POPCORN TO CANDY

In the autumn of 1950, Dorothy did not go home to Huddersfield to have her baby. She remained in the caravan and Reg peeped through the curtains until the midwife told him to make himself useful and help with the delivery. It was not normal for the father to see the birthing process, and it was a revelation to him. Their new daughter had a crop of dark hair and looked a little like Dorothy. They named her "Catherine Elaine" but called her "Candy".

Sweets were still rationed so selling popcorn on the market was a success and Reg earned more than he did as a hairdresser, except on rainy days, when few people ventured out.

"We ought to look at renting a house," suggested Dorothy. "There are some good ones in Southampton."

"What's wrong with living in the caravan?" asked Reg. "It doesn't cost us anything and it's better than paying rent."

"What's wrong? What's right?" asked Dorothy. "I've nappies to wash and we've no bath and no sink. Do you want to live in a caravan for the rest of your life, because I don't? We have to find something better."

"It's your fault you've another baby. We were happy before we had her," said Reg pointedly.

Dorothy, tried to make the best of a bad situation, realising Reg was still a boy and needed time to mature and grow into a man. She was bonded to him like a fly trapped in a spider's web. The spider came and went, but for her with no money and two small children, there was no escape. Too late, she understood her mother's warning and her own stupidity for rushing into marriage. When her daughters were older, she swore to herself, she would never criticise any young man they brought home and let their love affairs run their due course.

It was not all bad and Reg, never unhappy for long, was impulsive and often suggested on the spur of the moment, "Let's go out for the day to the seaside." In no time, Dorothy packed a picnic of jam sandwiches and flask of tea and laughing, they set off with Reg riding the motorbike and Dorothy in the sidecar squeezed in with their daughters. Their move south had been the one good thing she did not regret. Days out to pretty coastal towns, lazing on sandy beaches and trips to the New Forest were all to be enjoyed.

After a successful day on the markets, Reg returned home with several brown paper sacks. "I've done some shopping. Do you want to see?"

"Daddy, Daddy," called Susan running to her father. Reg picked her up and swung her around, kissing her on her forehead before putting her down again.

"Can we play trains?"

"Not now Susie."

"What have you bought?" asked Dorothy, suspiciously, opening the bags.

"Some sugar, butter and condensed milk," replied Reg, laughing.

"How?"

"A little negotiation on the black market. Have you noticed how sugar's much easier to buy now? Where's your cookery book?" Reg started to whistle, *We're off the see the Wizard.*

"You're up to something. You've got that silly look on your face."

"Have you ever tried making sweets?"

"Sweets? No, how could I? There's been a war and rationing for the last ten years."

"It's six years since the war to end all wars. People want to buy sweets and there's none in the shops so we can make our fortune."

"We can't make sweets. If you hadn't noticed, we live in an old bus with two children."

Reg ignored his wife and started to put various ingredients into the stew pan. After a while of stirring over the gas ring, he gave Dorothy the wooden spoon.

"Taste this. What do you think?"

"Tastes like ... fudge. But this is one idea too far. Why don't you stick at a proper job instead of flitting around. I never know when the next wage packet is coming in. I can't manage on nothing each week."

"Mmm, tastes really good. Do you want to hear my news? I can make coconut ice, toffee, fudge, peanut brittle, spearmints, rock –."

"What news?" interrupted Dorothy.

"I've bought a factory in Southampton. It's big enough to live in."

"I don't want to live in a factory. It's bad enough living in a bus," said Dorothy exasperated.

"An old man came up to me when I was on the market. He told me he used to run a factory before the war but had to close when they started rationing. Now they're lifting rationing, he doesn't want to start up again. He offered to sell it me for a fiver."

"I don't want to live in a factory. I want a house with two or three bedrooms, an inside bathroom with a bath and a toilet and a proper kitchen with a cooker and a kitchen sink. It's not much to ask."

Reg laughed. "Don't get mardy. It's got lots of equipment and you can sell sweets on the markets. It's a sweet factory."

"I don't know whether you noticed," said Dorothy. "There's no way I can go out with two children to look after."

"I'll take you to see it tomorrow. We can soon set it up and get it working again. What do you think Doe Doe?"

Dorothy could see Reg was excited. "It could be good," she agreed smiling at him.

"I've seen a large van we can buy. I can take you to the markets with the sweets and pick you up later."

"No Reg," protested Dorothy.

"I'll do some markets and between us, we should do really well."

Dorothy was reluctant but Reg was persuasive and once the factory was set up, she spent two days each week on a market, selling sweets, with Candy in her pram and Susan by her side. At four o'clock she would pack away her stall away and wait, sometimes for several hours, as Reg was invariably late.

"I'm hungry," complained Susan.

"I can't help it. Your Daddy's late again. I think he forgets about us," replied Dorothy.

"Why don't you put Daddy in the dustbin," suggested Susan who heard her mother often complain about him. "Then you could get a new Daddy."

"I supposed I could," said Dorothy smiling. "But you can't change Daddy by putting him in the dustbin. I think he would climb out."

Making and selling sweets earned them good money and Dorothy saved most of hers in a post office savings account and soon had enough to pay cash for a small, two up, two down terraced house in Mill Bank Street, Southampton. It was luxurious, compared to the old bus and had an upstairs bathroom and a kitchen with a sink and a gas cooker. Billy the Kid lived in the garden for a few weeks before being sold. Several days later, Reg returned home with a fluffy ball of black that purred and mewed as they stroked it.

"He's lovely," smiled Dorothy as the kitten cuddled up to her. "Black cats are supposed to be lucky. I think we'll call him Blackie. What do you think girls?" asked Dorothy as she stooped down.

"Can I hold him please?" asked Susan.

"Here, hold him gently and support his bottom with one hand so he feels safe and you can stroke him with the other."

Reg stopped to kiss Dorothy and smiled.

"I thought you'd like a kitten and he'll be good at catching mice. I've seen the odd one running about."

"Yes, so have I," agreed Dorothy.

*Photo:* Susan and Candy with Blackie

Reg sold his motorbike and bought himself his first, big black limousine car, an Austin 14 with leather seats and running boards. Two evenings a week, he played piano at the Wolston Railway Hotel and occasionally Dorothy went with him and sang a little. Recently, he had taken on a new singer, an attractive woman with bright red lipstick and dyed blond hair and Dorothy noticed Reg was taking particular care about his appearance.

Mrs Brown lived in the house next door and became like a grandmother to the two little girls and often volunteered to baby-sit so Dorothy could go with Reg to the club more often.

"What are you doing?" Reg asked as he saw Dorothy getting ready to go out.

"Mrs Brown is coming in to look after the girls so I thought I'd go with you for a night out."

"You don't have anything decent to wear," said Reg quietly. "I don't want you to come looking like that."

"What do you mean, looking like this?" replied Dorothy indignantly as she looked down at her drab dress and shoes. "I thought we wanted the same things in life. If we spend all our money on cars and clothes we'll never have anywhere better to live."

"I told you, I don't want to take you looking like that," replied Reg sharply as he went out of the door.

Dorothy returned to the small front living room and sat down with Mrs. Brown. "I'm not going," she said simply. "But I'll be going next time. Would you like a cup of tea?"

"That would be nice, thank you," said Mrs Brown, who had heard the conversation through the thin walls. "That husband of yours, he should be proud of his beautiful wife and children. Take no notice of him, a lot of young men don't know when they're well off."

The following day, Dorothy dressed the girls in their best clothes and left them to play in the garden while she tidied up and went to get herself dressed. By the shed were tins of left over paint. Susan, who had observed her father opening tins with a screwdriver, decided to do the same. She opened the lids and picking up the paintbrushes, began to do some decorating. She painted the fence, the garden shed, the tricycle and the pram. Blackie ran away as she ran towards him with the brush or he may have had a colour change. Candy stood watching and smiled when she said she would paint her like a wild west Indian. Just as Susan was completing her artistic endeavours, Dorothy came outside to collect them.

"Susie NO!" Dorothy shouted. "Put the brush down NOW." Susan did as she was told and stared guiltily at her mother. "Do not dare touch anything else," said Dorothy, standing at a safe distance away from her children. "Sit down on the grass and wait for your father to come back and sort you out."

Susan, not quite five years old, expected to be punished by having her bare bottom smacked. She sat quietly in anticipation of what was to come whilst Candy wailed. When Reg returned, he tried to

43

hide his amusement. He picked his daughters up and carried them, one under each arm, to the bathroom. Dorothy filled the bath with warm water and Reg soaped his daughters and tried to scrub off the paint, all the time chuckling to himself. He could not bring himself to reprimand Susan nor smack her. He rather liked having a mischievous daughter and would encourage her to be a tomboy.

Two days later, Dorothy went shopping and in the evening, Mrs Brown came round to baby-sit.

"Do you like my new outfit?" Dorothy asked as she put the finishing touches to her make-up. "I thought it was time I treated myself."

Reg said nothing but opened the door for her to accompany him to the hotel in his big black shiny car.

King George V1 died suddenly on 6th February 1952 and the BBC broadcast the news, followed by dismal funeral music. Princess Elizabeth was to be crowned queen the following year on 2nd June 1953.

"The new Queen is beautiful," commented Dorothy as she read the paper and looked at the photographs.

"Mmm," agreed Reg as he stirred sugar in the sugar bowl.

"I've written to my mother to invite her for a holiday."

Reg grimaced. "That's nice."

"I haven't seen her since Christmas and I thought we could take her out for days now you've bought a car."

"I could," replied Reg smiling. "But someone has to work."

"I've decided to stop working on the markets," Dorothy said quietly.

"You can't. We need you to sell the sweets or we won't earn enough money."

"It's impossible for me to carry on. I've been telling you for ages but you weren't listening. Candy is toddling and not in the pram and I can't keep an eye on them both while I'm serving sweets. You know how mischievous Susan is and Candy follows her everywhere. And then you keep us waiting for hours every night. You're never on time and I can't go on."

"You're always complaining."

"You try working the markets with two children," shouted Dorothy as her temper flared.

"Don't be ridiculous," retorted Reg, who was becoming angry. "How am I going to run the sweet factory and do more markets?"

"I don't care," shouted Dorothy defiantly. "From next week, I'm not doing the markets."

Reg grabbed hold of Dorothy's arm as they argued and smacked her across the face, knocking her to the floor. Dorothy twisted as she fell and felt a sharp pain in her back as well as stinging on her cheek." She looked up at Reg, her face contorted in pain.

"You shouldn't make me angry," he said turning away.

"And you shouldn't hit me," said Dorothy, quietly through clenched teeth as she struggled to get up. Grabbing her coat off the hook she slammed the front door and went to walk the streets. She had nowhere to go. She was too proud to leave Reg and return to Huddersfield and admit her marriage was a failure. Several hours later, Dorothy returned and ignoring Reg, she stayed in the kitchen.

There was a firm knock at the front door and Reg opened it.

"Mr. Calvert?" asked the policeman. "May I come in?"

Reg nodded and opened the door widely. The policeman sat down on the front room sofa and took off his helmet. He looked Reg directly in the eye.

"Your wife has made an allegation. I understand you've behaved violently towards her?"

"We had an argument," admitted Reg quietly. "She shouted at me."

"And you hit her?" asked the Policeman, getting out his notebook.

"Yes," replied Reg sheepishly.

"And you hit her across the face and she fell backwards?"

"Yes," replied Reg again, shocked by his own admission. And shocked by the realisation that Dorothy had reported him.

"Do you know it's against the law to cause grievous bodily harm?"

"Yes," replied Reg bleakly.

"Do you know it against the law to cause violence to your wife or children?"

"I hadn't thought," replied Reg, remembering the beatings in his own childhood.

"When a boy grows into a man, he has to learn how to control his temper. A man cannot go round hitting people just because they shout at him or he doesn't like them."

"I've never hit anyone else," replied Reg quietly.

"A man has to learn self-control or society would be a very violent place. And he has to learn to take care of his wife and children. Protect them. Not hit them."

"You're right," agreed Reg, embarrassed by his behaviour.

"Your wife has put in a complaint that when you hit her, she damaged her back. She's in a lot of pain."

"I didn't realise," said Reg.

"If you're reported again, by your wife or anyone else, we will have no choice but to charge and prosecute. You will go to court and may be sent to prison." The policeman continued to talk to Reg for several hours. He was experienced and this wasn't the first or last time he had intervened between man and wife. He was kindly by nature and if he could talk to the man, explaining the consequences of his actions, more often than not, the warning was sufficient to prevent further bad behaviour.

It was a salutary lesson. Never again did Reg raise his hand to hit Dorothy. He would clench his fists and keep them at his side. Instead, he learnt to walk away.

Dorothy, determined not to work on the markets, caused Reg a problem. He employed five ladies and made a variety of sweets, including coconut ice, macaroons and spearmints. He took free samples to all the sweet and tobacconist shops in and around Southampton and received regular orders to supply some of them.

"I've had a thought," said Reg.

"Oh yes," replied Dorothy quietly. Since their big argument she had become withdrawn, turned her back on him in bed and not spoken to him in conversation.

"I've seen an old butchers shop on the Northam Road, near the bridge.

"You mean by the new bridge they're building?"

"Yes. When it opens, the road will become busy with a good passing trade and ideal for a sweet shop. I could fit it out and you'd be able to stay at home with the girls and work in the shop."

Dorothy smiled in response

"We can go and look at it tomorrow and if you like it, I'll put an offer in."

Dorothy agreed to the shop and Reg worked hard, designing and fitting it out, making all the equipment himself. He was good at making things. Dorothy had a candy-striped overall and Reg a plain white one. Hartley's Sweet Shop was an immediate success. They stocked all the well-known brands of sweets and chocolates in addition to their own sweets. In addition Reg had an idea to sell hot salted peanuts. He found a large glass container, fitted an element underneath and added salt and the salesman from KP nuts was amazed at the amount of nuts they ordered. There was one problem; Dorothy began to work harder than before, seven days a week instead of two.

The shop opened at seven in the morning until nine at night. Most customers were regulars and Dorothy knew as soon as she saw them what sweets they wanted to purchase. Most of the sweets were contained in large glass jars on shelves and some were displayed in open in trays on the counter. Sweets and hot peanuts were sold in quarters, (four ounces) and Dorothy weighed the sweets on the scales and put them into a white paper bag.

Candy now aged three and very shy, often hid behind her mother's skirts if anyone strange talked to her. Her name was apt, she loved sweets and would steal them when no one was looking and stuff them in her mouth like a hamster and go and hide under the dining table to eat them.

"We have to do something to stop Candy stealing," said Dorothy concerned. "However much I tell her off she cannot resist eating sweets."

"Perhaps we should give both girls a little pocket money each day. A penny or two. If they want to spend it on sweets they can or if they save it, we can double the amount to give them an incentive to save," suggested Reg.

"Brilliant idea," agreed Dorothy smiling. "Perhaps they'll learn to save, like you did."

Reg laughed. "No one gave me pocket money when I was little. I had to earn my money."

"So did I, although Jim would give me the odd sixpence. It's odd that you never learned to save and I did."

"Opposites attract," replied Reg, squeezing her hand.

Occasionally, on sunny Sundays, Reg took his daughters out for the day on his own to his imaginary 'Never Never Land.' Hiring a boat, he rowed down the River Itchen and they sang at the top of their voices, *Row, row, row the boat,* or, *We're off to see the Wizard, the wonderful Wizard of Oz.* On one occasion, Reg took wire cutters with him and cut through barbed wire that had been stretched across the river to prevent access to the smaller by-waters. When they reached 'Never Never Land,' Reg tied up the boat to an overhanging branch of a willow tree and set about making a tent on the grassy bank from an old sheet. Reg sat under the tent and relaxed while he watched his daughters laughing and splashing as they ran naked in and out of the river. When they were hungry, he unpacked the bag Dorothy had provided and they feasted on jam sandwiches, Swiss roll, tinned fruit and drank dandelion and burdock.

## 1954 MUSIC TRENDS

*American actress and singer Doris Day had become a favourite and had hits with: "Secret Love," " The Black Hills of Dakota" and "If I Give My Heart to You". Johnnie Ray almost rocked with: "Such a Night." Crooners included Frank Sinatra with: "Three Coins in the Fountain." Nat King Cole: "Smile." Other Americans to top the charts included: Rosemary Clooney, Perry Como, Dean Martin and Frankie Laine.*

*British chart toppers included David Whitfield with: "Cara Mia," " The Book," " Santo Natale," "Rags to Riches" and "Answer Me." Trumpeter, Eddie Calvert, " Oh Mein Papa." Pianist, Winifred Atwell, "Lets Have Another Party" and "Rachmaninoff's 18th Variation on a Theme by Paganni." The Stargazers: "I See The Moon." Vera Lynn: "My Son My son." Petula Clark: "Little Shoemaker." Billy Cotton & His Band: "Friends and Neighbours." Comedians: Norman Wisdom: "Don't Laugh at Me." Max Bygraves: "Gilly Gily Ossenfeffer Katzenellen Bogen By the Sea."*

*Photo:* Rainy day street market.
Reg selling sweets inside the stall, his van behind.

*Photo:* 1953 Reg and Dorothy, Hartley's Sweet Shop, Northam, Southampton. Reg fitted out the former butcher's shop and they sold their own sweets plus famous brands, hot peanuts and cigarettes.

*Photo:* Camping weekend. Susan in the box, Candy on back seat.
(Car - Humber 16-50, built between 1928-1932)

# 6. SWEET RUIN

"Have you heard the Queen is coming to open Northam Bridge?"
asked Dorothy.

"No," replied Reg, who was busy repairing a second-hand
radiogram.

"I wish you wouldn't keep bringing old radiograms in. It's bad
enough living behind the shop without you filling the space with
electrical junk."

"It's not junk when I get it to work," replied Reg as he stood up
and pushed the brown plug into a socket. As he did so, the front lit
up and the speakers crackled. Reg turned the knob to tune in the
frequency to the BBC Light programme, "Workers Playtime."

"Turn it down," said Dorothy. "Can't hear myself think."

"There's an empty shop down the road. I could run a second-hand
electrical shop from there. Did I ever tell you how I used to
experiment with broadcasting when I was a boy? I had a link from
my bedroom to my friend in the next street. It was a bit hit and miss,
more miss than hit, but he did hear me. We had some fun
experimenting. How'd you fancy coming to Southampton Common
and listening to see if I can broadcast to you?"

"You're crazy," laughed Dorothy.

"I'm fascinated in how we can tune in and hear broadcasts from radio waves. It's amazing, all this sound coming from radio waves that zing through the air," said Reg.

"I suppose it is, but it would be even more amazing if you could tidy up your mess. I'm trying to sew the girls new dresses and I don't need your tools and electrical stuff all over the place."

"It'll be better when I open an electrical shop."

"Haven't you got enough to do with the factory and selling sweets? Why don't you stick to one thing at a time?"

"What d'you say?" asked Reg, who pretended not to hear above the noise of the radio.

"I thought I'd take a day off when the Queen comes. I expect there'll be thousands of people wanting to see her."

"Mmm. Thousands," agreed Reg. "The rent on the other shop isn't much and I won't need to fit it out. I can put a sign on the door and tell people to come down here if they want to buy anything."

"It's no good talking to you. What about concentrating on selling more sweets to other shops and running the sweet factory?"

"We could make sticks of rock," his mind jumping from radio to rock.

"Why sticks of rock?"

"Northam Bridge Rock. When the Queen comes we can promote the shop by giving away, say, five hundred sticks of rock. We'll have people queuing up to get inside the shop."

"I was going to close and have the day off."

"You said I should make more sweets. It'll be the busiest day of the year," smiled Reg.

The Queen came to visit Southampton on Saturday, 17th July 1954. It was a miserable, rainy day but an enthusiastic crowd came out to see the new queen and cheer her as she opened the bridge. The sign outside the shop advertised five hundred, free sticks of rock to be given away from twelve thirty. From twelve, a queue started to form outside the shop and by three pm, all the sticks of rock had gone.

Reg was in the habit of whistling wherever he went and Dorothy knew by the tune what sort of mood he was in. As he walked through the shop to the back room she heard the refrain *I see the moon and the moon sees me.*

"Guess what Doe Doe?"

"Tell me," replied Dorothy, smiling as he gave her a kiss.

"The manager of the Bannister Ballroom has asked me to be their compére."

"That's good. Will they pay you more than the Railway Hotel?"

"A bit more," replied Reg happily as he started to sing, *I see the moon and the moon sees me.* I can't get that tune out of my head. They're giving me a fairly free hand to build up their audiences and run competitions. And another thing, they've asked me to put together a new band so they can have their own house band."

"Do you know enough musicians?"

"I'll put feelers out," replied Reg happily, whistling again. He enjoyed compéring dances far more than running the sweet factory and to get a job at the prestigious Bannister Ballroom, was an achievement.

"Do you think you could help me more in the shop? I'm not feeling well. I'm sure there's something wrong with me."

"You should go to the doctors."

"I will if you could spend a morning in the shop while I go."

"I'm famished. What's for tea tonight?" asked Reg.

"An omelette, cauliflower and mash potatoes. You can look after the shop while I cook the meal."

"Sounds good," replied Reg, as he sat down and put his feet up, only to be disturbed a moment later by the shop bell ringing.

*Photo:* Reg Calvert – compére.

52

After the meal Reg changed into his dinner suit ready to go to the Railway Hotel. He was in high spirits and pleased with himself.

"You look so good in your dinner suit," said Dorothy.

"You look like a penguin," said Susan.

"He does a bit," agreed Dorothy smiling. "Bed you. And don't wake Candy up when you get in."

"Come on Doe Doe, put on a pretty dress and let's dance. It'll be like the old days."

"You mean before we were married and had children?" Dorothy removed her shop overall and Reg placed the 78 rpm record on the turntable of the radiogram and turned up the volume. "All of me" by Frank Sinatra blared out of the speakers and they laughed and danced around the shop.

"We haven't danced for ages," said Dorothy smiling. "But I've this pain in my side."

"Try this one," said Reg laughing as he put on Lonnie Donnegan's "Rock Island Line."

"How can anyone dance to skiffle?"

"Come on, it's fun," said Reg taking her hand.

"I can't dance to this. This pain in my side is getting worse."

"Come on Doe Doe, don't sit down."

"It's mad. I prefer to waltz or quickstep," said Dorothy stopping and holding her side.

"What's up? Is it a stitch?"

"No, it's not a stitch, it's worse than that. I think I'm going to be sick. I keep getting this pain and I'm so tired."

*Photo:* Reg as compére and entertainer.

53

"You should help me more," complained Dorothy. "Getting up at six in the morning and working till nine at night with two children to look after, meals to cook, and your shirts to wash and iron is too much for anyone."

"Don't go on so. Susan's at school so there's only Candy to look after."

"I don't want to live behind a sweet shop for the rest of my life. I want something better." said Dorothy slowly, rubbing her side and holding on to the shop counter.

"Come on, let's dance and you'll forget the pain. Have some fun," said Reg tugging at her hands.

"I can't. ...... the pain." Dorothy collapsed and Reg tried to pick her up and realised he must get help. He rushed out to the street and ran to the telephone box and rang 999. A few minutes later, Dorothy was carried away on a stretcher. Reg was bewildered. He was on his own. Dorothy was really ill. Her appendix had burst and doctors just managed to save her life.

Dorothy remained in hospital for two weeks and then went into a convalescence home for another two weeks. Reg had never worked so hard in his life. He had to run the shops, the factory, compére the dances and look after his two little girls. He was so pleased when he heard Dorothy was coming home. Each time the shop bell rang with customers, he became excited with anticipation. Eventually the shop bell rang and Dorothy entered, carrying her small brown leather suitcase, she called out, "I'm back everyone." Reg couldn't contain his happiness. He kissed her and carried her case into the back room.

"See who I've got? I told you Mummy was coming home today."

The girls ran to their mother and she knelt down to kiss them. "Are you all right? Has Daddy been looking after you okay?"

"He forgets to feed Blackie sometimes," replied Susan seriously, "But I remind him."

"Come on you two, let me get in to give your mother a love," said Reg, smiling widely as his little girls were hugged by Dorothy, one in each arm. "I really missed you Doe Doe. Getting up at six in the morning and working until nine at night with two children to look after is ... really hard."

Dorothy smiled and looked to the corner of the room. "I see you didn't manage the washing."

"Come and sit down and I'll make you a cup of tea."

Reg was like a new man, so good and understanding. It lasted for a whole three days. Then he slipped back into his old routine.

The traditional big confectioners resumed making sweets when rationing ended in 1953 and sweet shops, including their own, began to stock the well-known varieties, including Spangles, Rowntree's fruit gums and fruit pastels, Fry's chocolate creams, Cadbury's Dairy Milk Tray and Black Magic, Bluebird toffees, and many more varieties. Competing with the famous brands became more difficult and Reg changed his glucose supplier. Something went wrong and the sweets he made became rancid and all the shops he supplied wanted their money back. It broke his business and he was "ruined." Dorothy did her best to carry on but she was unwell and in desperation told Reg she would put the shop up for sale if he didn't help more. He ignored her threats until she gave him the letter. He read it slowly and then went very quiet.

"What have you done?"

"Dorothy bit her lip and tried to control her voice. "I told you. I've sold it."

"You've done what?" demanded Reg.

"I told you. I told you," said Dorothy defiantly. And then she broke down and started to sob. "You weren't listening to me."

"But it's a good business. It earned enough money to keep you and the girls."

"Great," replied Dorothy. "You get me working all hours so you don't have to worry. I told you we had someone interested. But you kept your head in a bucket of sand. We have two weeks to move."
Reg said nothing but sat at the kitchen table stirring sugar in the sugar bowl, round and round as Dorothy continued. "You've saved no money and we're broke and we can hardly live off what you earn compéring," said Dorothy raising her voice as she handed him the Southampton Echo. "There's lots of jobs advertised. So get off your backside and find a proper job. And you'd better find a job with accommodation and don't come back until you do."

Reg snatched the newspaper out of her hand and walked out slamming the door. As he went he called back sarcastically. "Good bye."

For a night and a day Reg stayed away. Dorothy carried on, like a ghost walker, serving customers and trying to smile. Doubts flickered across her mind. What was she to do if he didn't come back? How was she going to manage with two young children? Then, she heard him whistling as if nothing had happened.

"Hello Doe Doe, would you like a cup of tea?"

"No thank you," replied Dorothy icily.

"Do you want a piece of toast?" he asked as he took three slices of white bread and placed them under the grill.

"No thank you."

"I'm famished. I haven't eaten since yesterday."

"That's your problem," replied Dorothy tartly.

"Do you want to hear my news," asked Reg mischievously?

"What news," asked Dorothy, suspiciously?

"I found a job. I went for an interview in Romsey. You'll like it. And we'll have a nice flat above the shop."

"What shop?"

"There's a beautiful abbey in Romsey," continued Reg.

"What shop?" repeated Dorothy.

"I'm going to be a Television and Radio Engineer," grinned Reg.

"But you don't know anything about televisions."

"I managed to talk my way into the job. I know a lot about radios and repairing radiograms so it won't take me long to learn about televisions. Since the Queen's Coronation, everyone wants a television and no one knows how to fix them," explained Reg as he put his arm around Dorothy's waist to give her a hug but she rebuffed his affection, hiding her pleasure that he had come back by turning her head away.

# 7. ROMSEY

In July of 1956, the Calvert family moved to Romsey. Tait's Television and Radio shop was in the centre of the small market town and above the shop was a spacious two bedroom flat with a modern bathroom and toilet. For the first time since their marriage Dorothy was content. Reg had a regular nine to five job earning nine pounds a week. He became a very good engineer and Dorothy was proud of him. At last she had what she wanted, somewhere nice to live and a husband who gave her his wage packet.

Once Reg mastered the art of repairing radios and televisions he began to get bored and looked for new opportunities.

"I'm going to start my own dance at the Drill Hall," announced Reg as he ate cheese and pickle sandwiches, drank tea and smoked a cigarette during his lunchtime break.

Dorothy looked surprised. "I thought you were happy with this job?"

"I am, but I need something else to do and we could do with a little more money," smiled Reg. "I've booked the hall to start in a couple of week's time, once I've arranged a band and organised a sound system."

"It could be good," agreed Dorothy. "There's not much else going in Romsey."

"And I'm thinking of renting offices in Southampton. I've seen some in Portland Terrace, near the Civic Centre. I thought I could start a shop fitting business."

"How on earth are you going to manage that and be an engineer, and run a dance?"

"I thought you could help in the office sometime, now both girls are at school," smiled Reg.

"That's the trouble with you. You're always thinking," replied Dorothy returning his smile. "When are you going to have time to make up the orders that come in?"

"I've plenty of time. It doesn't take long to repair televisions and I like making and designing things. I thought I would call the business, Hartex," grinned Reg.

"I suppose I could help now both girls are at school."

Reg established a regular weekly dance in Romsey and attracted a good crowd. He also opened an office with a sign by the door saying "Hartex Shop fitters." Orders came in intermittently and Dorothy caught the bus to Southampton and dealt with enquiries.

"I think I'll buy myself a car," said Reg.

"Why, asked Dorothy? "What's wrong with using Tait's van?"

"I've seen a Buick. It's beautiful, my dream car, a limousine with running boards, real leather upholstery and walnut dashboard; it has everything.

"How much," asked Dorothy?

"Never you mind," replied Reg, waving a wad of notes in his hand. "The Romsey dance is doing well."

"You could let me have that," laughed Dorothy trying to take the money off him as he lifted his hand out of her reach.

"You have my wages each week. The extra I earn is mine," laughed Reg.

The River Test wound around Romsey and sometimes the family walked to the river and lazed on the bank. Reg enjoyed swimming and his trunks were hand-knitted in maroon wool. Clutching his towel round his waist he wriggled into them and took a running leap into the clear running water, hanging onto his trunks as he did so.

"The water's lovely, why don't you come on in?"

"You're welcome, I'll watch you," replied Dorothy as she undressed the girls and let them run naked down the muddy bank.

"Can you see any little fish?" called Reg.

"Lots," giggled Susan. "But they keep swimming away from my toes."

"Can you see any big fish?" called Reg.

"No," answered Susan, peering through the crystal clear water and in between the reeds.

"Watch the big fish don't eat your toes," called Reg.

"Don't be silly Reg, you're frightening Candy. She won't go in the water now," said Dorothy, kicking off her sandals and leading Candy down to the water's edge.

"I was only joking," replied Reg laughing as he took Susan up in his arms and demonstrated how to do the breaststroke. "Here, hold my hand Candy and I'll show you how to swim."

After an hour or so, Dorothy called her daughters. "Come on, it's time to get out, you're turning blue. It's rub-a-dub-dub time and then you can have your picnic," said Dorothy, holding out two towels.

Laid out on a red and white gingham cloth were fish paste sandwiches, home made bramble jelly sandwiches, tinned peaches and tinned cream. Reg emerged from the river but his trunks were so heavy with water they slid down to his knees.

"Here, have a towel," laughed Dorothy. "Before you show the world what you've got."

"Bbrrr, it's cold when you stop," said Reg as he waded out of the water.

Childhood illnesses, chicken pox, mumps and German measles, were diseases all children were encouraged to catch from other contagious children, as infection in an adult would be far more serious. Measles, however, was to be avoided if at all possible. Susan caught it and became very ill with a high temperature and fever. The doctor was called out several times and she stayed in a darkened room as even a small crack of light hurt her eyes. As she began to recover, Dorothy borrowed schoolbooks and to her surprise, discovered Susan, who was now eight years old, could not read or write. It was the first time Dorothy had made time to help with Susan's schoolwork as her school reports were always glowing. Only then did she discover that the primary school in Southampton had been experimenting with new teaching methods. Dorothy set about teaching Susan herself and when she returned to school three weeks later, she had mastered it.

Their cat, Blackie, had settled in well with them in the flat, catching mice that dared to scuttle across the floor. One of the neighbours left his catch of minnows and sticklebacks in a saucer and Blackie ate them. When he did not come in for his meal Dorothy searched for him and found him in the back yard, laid out and almost lifeless. Heartbroken, she picked up her cat and carried him into the flat and tried to get him to drink water before taking him to the vets. Nothing could be done to save him. The vet thought the sticklebacks were poisonous and Blackie died.

Reg, on his travels in the van, found an injured raven with a damaged wing by the roadside and brought it home for Dorothy to nurse back to health. They could see it was an intelligent bird and had quite a character. It lived in the bathroom for two days. On the third day they discovered it, drowned, head first down the toilet.

Ada wrote to Reg, a short note to let him know her mother was seriously ill and Reg should return to Huddersfield immediately to see her. Shortly after receiving the note, the telephone rang in the shop. Mr Tait handed the mouthpiece to Reg and Ada gave Reg the dreaded news. Lilia had died.

Emotion welled up inside of Reg as he went upstairs to tell Dorothy. With tears running down his cheeks, Dorothy immediately guessed and they clung to each other, rocking backwards and forwards as they both cried.

"Would you like a cup of tea or coffee?" asked Dorothy.

"Nothing thanks," replied Reg as he sat down at the kitchen table and stared into space. "There was no time to go and see her," he said wiping his eyes. "She was the best mother anyone could ever have. I should have gone home more often to see her."

"She was an angel," said Dorothy, wiping her tears. "I can't believe she won't be there any more. They say bad luck runs in three. First Blackie and then the raven and now...." Dorothy's words trailed away.

"She never said a cross word to me. I don't know what would have happened to me if she hadn't been there. No one else would have looked after me. They never called me by my name, they used to say, "Where's the bastard?" but she never did. I was always her Reggie."

"I didn't know," said Dorothy quietly, putting her arms around his shoulders to console him as he sobbed quietly.

"I should have gone to see her more often. Will you come up to the funeral with me?"

"Of course," replied Dorothy.

Tom arranged the funeral and Reg returned with Dorothy and their daughters to Huddersfield, Reg staying with his Dad and Ada, Dorothy and the girls, with her mother. The family were pleased to see 'our Reggie' and it was obvious to Dorothy, that they were proud of him.

A few months after the funeral, Tom moved house and bought a small, stone built hillside cottage in Elland. For the first time, he chose to live in a house without a basement and gave up his life's work, sold his tools and engineering equipment and never completed his invention to make a machine that could work on perpetual motion.

*Photo (top):* 1956 Romsey. Dorothy, Susan and Candy. (Buick car)
*Photo (below):* 1957 Dorothy outside 44 Portland Terrace.
(Sheerline car loaded up for the dances)

# 8. ROCK AROUND THE CLOCK

## 1955 MUSIC TRENDS

*The 1955 hit parade comprised mainly of big bands, ballads and country music. American singers dominated the charts and included: Tony Bennett, Frank Sinatra, Frankie Laine, Nat King Cole, Dean Martin, Johnny Ray, Doris Day, Eartha Kit and Pat Boone. The most popular singer in UK charts was Ruby Murray, from Ireland. There were a few British chart toppers, Alma Cogan, Dickie Valentine, trumpet player - Eddie Calvert, radio presenter - Jimmy Young and comedian - Max Bygraves.*

*There was one American singer with a new kind of music Reg had never heard before. He purchased the record, not knowing then, it would change his life forever. "Rock Around The Clock," by Bill Haley and the Comets.*

**\*\*\*\*\***

Reg was out working most evenings and had grown in confidence and got a real buzz from running his own dance, compéring the dances at the Bannister Ballroom and entertaining the crowd at the Railway Hotel. He was quite striking in his dinner suit with tails and his charisma and entertainment skills had greatly increased the audience. After introducing two musicians, he left the stage and walked into the crowd, as he often did, to chat to the regulars.

"Would you like a drink?" asked one young man.

"No thanks," replied Reg. "Not while I'm working. I've a cup of tea waiting for me in the office."

"I'm Terry Scott," said the young man, holding out his hand. Reg took it and they shook hands amiably. "You put on a good show."

"Thanks," smiled Reg.

"The last time I came to the Railway Hotel it was almost empty. You've really built it up."

"That must have been some time ago. Yes, there's a good atmosphere," agreed Reg warmly.

"It was. I'm either out working or my wife expects me to be at home on the nights I'm not," winked Terry.

"Are you a musician?"

"I play guitar and sing, ballads, skiffle and other things."

"On your own or with a band?" enquired Reg.

"Depends. On my own or sometimes as part of a trio in the clubs."

"How do you get away with that?"

"We hide the drummer behind a curtain or a sheet," replied Terry laughing.

"And you've never been caught?"

"The police come in and know what we're doing but turn a blind eye. Tell the landlord not to do it again," replied Terry.

"The law's an ass," smiled Reg. "Why we can't have more than two musicians in a club or pub is beyond me."

"One club got caught a couple of week's ago and prosecuted. The headline news was 'Four Beats in a Bar.'"

"Very funny," grimaced Reg. "Dance halls can have musicians but no alcohol. Clubs can have a bar but only two musicians. The law is crazy. Do you play guitar for a living?"

"No. I Wish. My wife wouldn't approve. I'm on the docks but it's good to earn a bit extra, especially when they lay us off in the summer. I normally play at the Pier on Wednesday nights."

"I know, for Len Canham. I'll try to get to see you one week," replied Reg warmly, as he made his exit to the office to drink his tea.

Reg had made the acquaintance of Len Canham who was an exuberant character, portly, in middle years with a partiality for attractive young boys. He lived with his mother in a splendid apartment above the pier and his constant companion was Stevie, a golden retriever. Len was good at organising his own entertainment so did not need a compére but he enjoyed Reg's company and the two men got on well together.

Reg made a point of going to see Terry Scott perform. He had taken a liking to him and was impressed by his easy, relaxed persona and the way he crooned, in the style of Bing Crosby and Frank Sinatra.

"You play well," complimented Reg.

"Thanks," replied Terry.

"I'm looking for a guitarist next week. I need someone to accompany me on the piano."

"Where? At the Railway Hotel?"

"No, I've started a gig at Broughton Village Hall near Romsey."

"Okay. I'll give it a go," agreed Terry.

Broughton hall was deserted when Terry arrived, except for a lady cashier waiting by a table in the foyer and Reg, sitting on stage and playing the piano, badly. He was being accompanied by a tape recorder backing track, amplified through loudspeakers. Terry stopped in the doorway in astonishment. He had never seen anyone play to a backing track.

"Hi. Good to see you," Reg called out as he continued to play.

"No audience?" asked Terry.

"Not yet, they'll be here soon," replied Reg casually. "I don't have a piano at home so I'm rehearsing with myself."

"The tape recording idea is fantastic. You're a genius. I've never seen anything like it," said Terry.

Reg grinned in response.

"Who else is on tonight?"

"The drummer should arrive soon to make up our trio and we have the "Ray Waller Townsmen" with a pretty girl singer called Carol Laine."

"Sounds good," replied Terry as he wired up to the amplification system using matchsticks to hold the wires in position. "Did you make the speakers yourself?"

"Yes," replied Reg, helping with the wires. "They're bigger and give out a better sound than most of the ones you can buy."

Terry tuned his guitar and he and Reg started to jam together, having fun. Ten minutes later, the doors were flung open and the audience arrived. Reg had organised local bus transport from all the surrounding villages and soon the hall was humming to the sound of music and happy dancers.

Most days, Reg returned home in the lunch breaks to spend time with Dorothy. When she heard him spring up the stairs, two steps at a time whistling gaily *Secret Love,* she knew he was in a good mood. He flung open the door and greeted her with a kiss.

"What's that you've bought?" asked Dorothy as he waved a package in the air.

"Just listen to this," replied Reg as he placed the 78-rpm record on the radiogram and set the needle over the first groove. *Rock around the Clock* by Bill Haley erupted from the record player. "Isn't it great? It's wild. There's never been anything like it. It's called Rock & Roll."

"Rock and Roll?" repeated Dorothy. "It's loud. Turn it down."

"It'll soon catch on. I've asked the man in the record shop to import all the Rock and Roll he can find. The American government doesn't like it and the BBC won't play it. We should have free radio instead of Housewives Choice and Mrs Dale's Diary." Reg took Dorothy's hand and tried to show her how to jive. They kicked off their shoes and laughed.

"I've got an idea," said Reg as they danced.

"Not another?"

"I want to run more dances. We have to find a way to bring Rock and Roll to England. Run dances for teenagers."

"Teenagers?" enquired Dorothy, "What's a teenager?"

"A teenager is aged between thirteen and nineteen. A 'teenager.' Maybe we can bring in bands from the USA."

"No Reg, we've no money to pay for bands. What would you like for lunch? You can have Spam, fish paste or cheese."

"Cheese and pickle please."

"I saw you this morning."

"Yes," replied Reg, thinking back. "I had a few calls in Romsey. Mrs Ditton bought a new television last week. She didn't know how to work it so I showed her how to turn the knobs. And then I had to fit an aerial above the green grocer's shop."

"That's where I saw you, but you didn't see me. You were running across the roof like a monkey. I stood and watched you with my hand across my mouth, hardly daring to breathe in case you fell."

"You needn't have worried," replied Reg, putting his arm around her and giving her a kiss.

"I do worry. You've no fear of anything. An old man came and stood by me and asked if I knew you? When I said I did, and that you were my husband, he said he hoped I had you well insured because you wouldn't live long."

"Nice. I've got an idea. What if?"

"What if pigs could fly?" interrupted Dorothy, laughing again.

"What if I put together my own Rock and Roll bands? I should be able to find young guitarists and singers from the skiffle bands around."

"You can't Reg. We haven't any money saved. What if we stayed here in Romsey with you doing a proper job? It's the first time we've been a real family."

"There's no such word as can't and I'm already earning more from the dances than Mr Tait pays me."

"Here, have your lunch or you'll be late back to work."

"Don't get grumpy," said Reg as he unfolded a map and spread it across the table and pointed. "Look, Doe Doe. All these big towns, Eastleigh, Portsmouth, Winchester, Salisbury, Andover, Basingstoke, Newbury and lots more."

"So."

"We can run rock 'n' roll dances up and down the country. There's no one else running dances for teenagers."

"It's no use talking to you. There's no such word as can't in your dictionary. Once you've an idea you're like a dog with a bone. You keep gnawing at it until you find a way to make it work. You don't care about me, or the children, or whether I'm happy or not. This has been the best year of my life and you want to move on. Why can't you be like other men and settle down? You're twenty-eight years old and it's time to settle down and accept life as it is."

"I'm going to give my notice in but I'll wait until I've got things established."

"No Reg, why can't we stay here? You're such a good engineer and we've been really happy in Romsey. We're comfortably off. Much better than most people and we should be able to buy a really nice house if you were to save your money."

"There's no point in working for someone else when I'm doing much better on my own," replied Reg smoking a cigarette and stirring sugar in the sugar bowl. "Would you like a cigarette?"

"Thanks," replied Dorothy taking one. "Where are we going to live?"

"There's some new houses being built at Chandlers Ford. I'll take you to see them."


Reg persisted in his ambition to run more dances and he booked halls at Christchurch and Toton and ran them as ballroom dances but combined them with skiffle groups and rock 'n' roll records in the breaks. There were no local musicians who knew how to play "rock" and he realised he would need to encourage and train musicians to have the sort of music he wanted.

The promise of a new house pacified Dorothy but when they went to view, neither of them liked the properties.

"They would do for the moment," said Dorothy looking hopefully at Reg.

"We'll find somewhere better." replied Reg, giving her hand a squeeze.

"Like what?" asked Dorothy exasperated. "We've to leave the flat next week."

"We can move into Portland Terrace until we find somewhere else."

"They're offices for Hartex and not suitable for a home."

"Better than living in a caravan," joked Reg. "There's a ground floor toilet and a sink in the kitchen."

"It's a dump. It doesn't even have a bathroom."

"It does, in the outhouse," said Reg cheerfully.

"There's no way I'm using that!" exclaimed Dorothy.

"I'll buy a zinc bath and hang it on the wall. It's only for a short time until I've made more money."

"Great," retorted Dorothy.

"It's big enough and you could run a print works from the ground floor rooms," said Reg nonchalantly.

"Me, run a print works!" exclaimed Dorothy. "Why should I want to run a print works?"

"To print tickets and posters for the dances," replied Reg smiling knowingly. "And I've seen a second-hand Heidelberg printing machine. It's going cheap."

"I don't want to be a printer. It's a man's trade."

"Anything a man can do, you can do better, or so you keep telling me," laughed Reg.

"I don't know anything about printing or typesetting," replied Dorothy even more disgruntled. She could see where this conversation was leading.

"We'll soon learn," replied Reg.

"No Reg," replied Dorothy huffily.

"Give's a kiss and don't be so grumpy," he said gently, putting his arms around her. "The World's our oyster."

# 9. PORTLAND TERRACE

## 1956 MUSIC TRENDS

*From the U.S.A., came Elvis Presley. He looked sexy and sensational and hit the charts with "Hound Dog" and "Heartbreak Hotel." Bill Haley and the Comets looked staid and old fashioned but their music was new and exciting. Their hits included "Rock Around the Clock" and "See You Later Alligator." By contrast, beautiful ballads sung by "crooners" also topped the charts. The Platters: "The Great Pretender," "My Prayer" and "Only You." Other crooners included: Frank Sinatra, Dean Martin, The Four Aces, Nat King Cole and Louis Armstrong.*

*British music was one step, or even two, behind the U.S.A. The Goons reached the top with: "I'm Walking Backwards for Christmas" and "The Ying Tong Song." Johnny Dankworth had his first hit with "Experiments with Mice." Frankie Vaughan "crooned" his way to the top and Lonnie Donegan skiffled, "Rock Island Line" and "Lost John."*

*****

Dorothy and Reg packed their few possessions into a borrowed van and moved into 44 Portland Terrace, Southampton, in the summer of 1956. As they arrived, they heard the chimes from the clock tower at the Civic Centre ring out "O God Our Help In Ages Past," as it did on the hour, every hour. The four storey Victorian terraced house had seen better days and stood in the middle of a dilapidated row of houses. One end of the terrace had been bombed during the war and all that remained were cavernous basements in the hillside set in scrubby wasteland.

Reg unlocked the front door and between them they carried their furniture up the stairs.

"I'll not manage the beds," said Dorothy puffing as she climbed the stairs holding one end of a settee with Reg pushing from behind.

"No problem," replied Reg. "You're stronger than you look."

"I'll certainly get fit, running up and down three or four flights of stairs," said Dorothy pausing to get her breath and looking down at the floor. "Brown lino everywhere, reminds me of the war and everything being utility."

"It's better than floorboards," replied Reg putting his hand in his pocket and taking out a wad of notes. "You can make the lounge homely. Buy a rug for the floor and some new furniture."

"That won't buy much," said Dorothy smiling and holding her hand out for more. She had no intention of staying in Portland Terrace but was pleased to receive money to buy new furniture. "I've seen some modern red and grey settees and I can decorate the lounge with red Chinese style wallpaper to match them."

Reg delved in his pocked and gave her some extra money. He was in a good humour and pleased to pacify her. This was the first day of his new life.

The lower ground floor led to an out-house bathroom and a raggle taggle garden with yellow flowering ragwort and dandelions. Reg had already installed the Heidelberg print machine into the back office on the ground floor and wooden trays stacked with various typefaces and typesetting tools were laid out in the front office. The first and second floor became their living quarters. The rooms were a good size and Dorothy set about making the best of them as a temporary measure until they moved again.

Reg visited various print works, chatting to printers and typesetters, asking questions and observing how things were done. He quickly learnt the trade and explained to Dorothy what to do. Years of helping his Dad in the basement build his invention meant he understood engineering and enjoyed getting the big old machine to work again. Dorothy found she actually enjoyed the printing trade and was nimble at typesetting and had an artistic eye to design layouts. A new sign was put outside the front door, 'Hartex Printers and Shop Fitters.' In the autumn, Dorothy enrolled at Southampton Art College to learn how to typeset professionally. She was the first woman on the course and only allowed because she was self-employed. At the end of the course she was not permitted to take the exam and qualify, as printing and typesetting were a "man's trade.

The luxury Buick car was exchanged for a more practical Austin Sheerline. It was still a limousine but larger, could easily seat five or six passengers and carry loud speakers and equipment in the boot and on the roof. To publicise the dances, Reg fitted a loudspeaker onto the top of the car and drove around playing rock 'n' roll music and announcing forthcoming dances. After each dance, he mixed a bucket of wallpaper paste and put it in the rear of the car, then, making sure no one was about, he surreptitiously stuck "Teen Beat Party Night" posters in every available location. Lampposts, empty shop doorways and windows, on billboards and covered up other people's posters with his own if they in competition to him.

Reg, in his element, focussed on building up his entertainment business. He toured the south coast, making enquiries and inspecting all kinds of village halls, town halls, drill halls and ballrooms and booked suitable ones on a regular weekly basis. Musicians who played the right kind of music were harder to find and he searched everywhere, going to the 2i's Coffee Bar in Soho and encouraging local skiffle groups to start playing rock 'n' roll.

After several months, Dorothy realised there were strange happenings and sounds emanating from the basement of the house. Something walked up and down the stairs at night.

"Did you walk up the stairs and put the electric fire on in the lounge?" asked Dorothy as Reg undressed and climbed into bed next to her.

"No. I've been sitting on the toilet reading the Melody Maker."

"I heard you walk up the stairs and turn the fire on," replied Dorothy.

"Must be your imagination," laughed Reg.

"I heard something. I keep on hearing strange noises in the night."

"Don't be silly. It's probably mice, we need another cat."

"Are you going to check to see whether the fire's on?" asked Dorothy.

"No. I'm in bed now."

"Okay. I'll go," replied Dorothy reluctantly. Several minutes later she returned and climbed into bed, putting her cold feet on Reg.

"You've got ice blocks instead of feet."

"The fire was on. You must have done it," said Dorothy. "Fires don't switch on by them selves."

"We must have a ghost," joked Reg.

The strange sound of someone walking up and down the stairs became a regular occurrence and then one morning, as they lay in bed, they heard someone walking in the basement.

"We've got burglars," said Reg sitting up sharply and listening. "You go down and investigate and I'll keep watch from the window with my rifle."

"Don't go shooting anyone," warned Dorothy as she hurriedly put on her slippers and dressing gown.

"No. I'll make them stand still with their hands up," said Reg as he got his gun and opened the rear window overlooking the garden.

"Sounds like they're opening the back door," said Dorothy. "Can you see anyone?"

"No," replied Reg.

Dorothy quickly and quietly went down the stairs and looked in both basement rooms. There was no one. The back room was icy cold and she shivered. The normally locked and bolted rear door was wide open. Dorothy looked out and called up to Reg. "Did you see anyone?"

"No one."

"We must have a ghost," said Dorothy as she was getting dressed in the bedroom. "It was icy cold in the back room.'

"There's no such thing as ghosts," replied Reg laughing.

"How do you know?" asked Dorothy.

"I don't. I'll tell you what. I'll fit a door between the basement and the ground floor and see if it stops whatever it is from walking up and down the stairs."

Susan and Candy were happy living in Portland Terrace and enjoyed their new lifestyle, sometimes travelling with their father when he was looking for dance halls and other times, going out at night to a dance and being introduced to famous stars. During the day when they were not at school, they were permitted to roam the streets and parks of Southampton with neighbourhood children, mostly boys.

Everywhere was the remnants of war. Basements of bombed out houses at the end of the road were like caves in the hillside. Empty shells of houses stood with boarded up windows and keep-out signs. Tramps lived in the empty houses and the children, having no fear, ignored "No Trespass" signs and entered through creaking doors, picking their way over rubble and climbed up ramshackle stairs to walk stretcher beams like tight ropes, from one room to another. Dorothy made Susan responsible for looking after her younger sibling and instructed them to "stick together" and reminded them often, "don't go home with any men, don't take sweets from men, and don't talk to the road sweeper."

As 1956 drew to an end, Reg was planning the Christmas and New Year dances. If they were good and he made more money, he would re-invest in his business and think about employing people to help. He was travelling a road of his own making and knew where he wanted to go but was often distracted and took diversions and wrong turnings. He knew it would take another year or two, but he would get there, and, bring rock 'n' roll to England.

Dorothy was planning a different journey. To Huddersfield by train, to visit her family to celebrate Christmas and New Year while Reg remained at home to run the dances. As she reflected on the year, she knew it had been a mistake to leave Romsey. Their lives had been perfect. When Dorothy complained about the house or lack of housekeeping, Reg shrugged his shoulders and remained quiet, accepting her battering of words like rain hammering on a glass windowpane. No matter what she said, it rarely penetrated through to the interior consciousness of his mind.

### 1957 MUSIC TRENDS

*Elvis Presley was "All Shook Up" and continuing to cause a sensation but Paul Anka's song, "Diana" sold the most records in 1957. The Everly Brothers and Little Richard were also 'shaking up' the music scene. Crooners and ballad singers had moved over but not out of the charts and included Johnny Ray, Harry Belafonte, Nat King Cole, Andy Williams, Peggy Lee and Bing Crosby.*

*British music was still several steps behind the U.S.A. In London, theatre impresario, Larry Parnes discovered Tommy Steel in the 2i's coffee bar. Tommy could rock' but was a poor imitation of Elvis. Other British singers to make the top twenty included Lonnie Donegan, Petula Clarke and Frankie Vaughan.*

*Photo:* Dorothy, Susan and Candy enjoying a day at the seaside.

1957, The new year came in and Reg worked harder than ever. Len Canham and Reg now had much in common, sharing the same groups and singers at their various dances. They socialised and afternoon tea at the Pier with Len and his mother was a delight as she made the most wonderful cakes. Another time, they went together to Stonehenge where they picnicked and wandered freely among the standing stones with hardly another person about.

Reg liked to bring animals home for Dorothy and his daughters. A beautiful grey kitten, cross Siamese and Abyssinian with tabby markings on her forehead and an underbelly of orange marmalade fur was rejected by the breeders and given to Susan who immediately fell in love with her and named her Katy. A tiny Dutch, black and white rabbit was so small, Dorothy had to bottle-feed it. Reg promised to build a hutch ready for the time it was weaned but the hutch was never built. "Bunny" was house-trained and lived in the kitchen and became the best of friends with Katy. A wild baby rabbit, shot with a small pellet, was nursed by the girls but only survived for three days, in their wardrobe. A tiny hedgehog was kept as a pet in the bathroom outhouse and Susan took it for walks and fed it on worms, beetles, bread and milk, raw eggs and strawberry desert.

Reg never stopped surprising Dorothy or making her worry. One morning, after he had eaten his breakfast, he continued to sit at the table, stirring sugar in the sugar bowl, round and round while he drank coffee, smoked and contemplated his next big project. Dorothy could see his mind ticking over.      Do you want another cup of coffee?" Dorothy asked, trying to break into his thoughts.

"No thanks, wouldn't mind another piece of toast though."

"With marmalade or home-made bramble jelly?"

"Bramble jelly, of course," smiled Reg. "What do you think about me holding a Rock Festival in the New Forest this summer?"

"A Rock Festival, what do you mean?"

"Like a dance, but with lots of bands and to have it outside in the open air. It can run all night instead of being restricted to closing at ten thirty. I can just imagine it in the forest. It will be fantastic," enthused Reg.

"Risky," replied Dorothy.

"If I sell advance tickets, even if it rains, I won't lose everything," replied Reg thoughtfully.

"You'll have to organise all sorts of things.      Toilets. Food. Stewards," said Dorothy.

"You're right," agreed Reg. "I'll make enquiries today and see how much it will cost to book a site."

"How will people get there?" asked Dorothy.

"I can organise coaches," replied Reg smiling.

"You can only get about forty people on each coach. How many will you need to cover costs?"

"Not sure, I'll have to think," replied Reg, making some mental calculations.

"What about having a family holiday this year? The four of us together, we've never been on a family holiday."

"Life's one long holiday when you're enjoying yourself. I don't need a holiday," replied Reg smiling. "I think I would need twenty or thirty coaches."

"I thought we could go to Butlins," persisted Dorothy. "The new camp at Clacton is supposed to be very good."

"You go with the girls," suggested Reg. "You'll enjoy it."

"I'd rather you came," said Dorothy sulkily.

"Good morning campers," laughed Reg.

"It's not camping. You have your own hut and there's entertainment, shows, and they cook all the meals."

"It's not my sort of holiday. I prefer camping in the New Forest. I'll take the girls away soon. Why don't you come with us?"

"What! And sleep in a cardboard box? No thanks. I need my bed. My back hurts too much to go camping. Dr Busk is making me an appointment with a back specialist to see if they can do anything to improve it. He thinks traction might help."

"Mmm," agreed Reg who had lost interest in the conversation.

"I suppose I could ask my mother to come and stay. She might like to go to Butlins."

"Good thinking," agreed Reg.

The summer holidays brought various family visitors. First, Dorothy's mother came, travelling by coach from Huddersfield to Southampton. Dorothy booked a week at Butlins in a stand for independence as Reg had resolutely refused to go so. When they arrived, Dorothy was disappointed. The small hut was basic with uncomfortable beds in a long line of other wooden huts, the weather cold and the food bland. She did not ask to go again. Next, Ada came to stay for a few days when she was on a concert tour. A small, plump woman with a large bosom, she greeted everyone effusively and the two girls were surprised that someone they only remembered seeing once, should be so sloppily affectionate towards them. She was totally opposite to their other aunts and grandmother, who restrained their affections. Dorothy disliked her immensely but tried not to show it but Reg was pleased she had come and took great pride in showing her what he was doing with his life.

"It's time your girls started to learn the piano," suggested Ada. "We're a musical family and they ought to have a piano."

"You're right," agreed Reg, smiling thoughtfully.

"They're growing so quickly, they ought to start soon."

Reg bought two pianos. One for the front room and the other for the dining room and Dorothy purchased Roland Piano Tutors. Both parents spent a little time teaching their daughters how to play the pieces and read music.

Tom Calvert was invited for a winter holiday and the two girls were excited. They loved to see their granddad. He was like Father Christmas without the white beard and wore a smart, three-piece suit that had a pocket in his waistcoat with a gold watch tucked inside with only the chain showing on the outside. A raconteur, he loved to tell his pretty little granddaughters fantastic stories as they sat, one on each knee.

"When Granddad comes, you haven't to get into bed with him for a cuddle," warned Dorothy.

"Why not," asked Susan?

"Because he has shingles."

"What's that," asked Susan?

"It's a type of rash. And you don't want to catch it," warned Dorothy.

Susan was in the habit of getting up early most mornings to do her piano practice in the dining room.

"Susie" called Tom quietly. He was in the lounge on the bed settee with the door ajar.

"Yes," replied Susan, hesitating by the door.

"Come and have a cuddle," invited Tom, lifting the blankets.

"I can't," replied Susan nervously.

"Why not lass?" asked Tom, smiling at her.

"Mummy said you had spingles and it's conjajous and I might catch it," replied Susan honestly.

"Nay lass, you mean Shingles. I haven't got any spots. See. That was a long time ago and I'm better now. Come and have a cuddle," said Tom again, lifting the bedclothes and Susan climbed in as Tom put his arm around her and cuddled her affectionately.

"Would tha like to know how bairns are made?"

"Yes," replied Susan innocently.

"All ladies have a hole, just here," explained Tom, touching hers while stroking and rubbing her gently up and down. It wasn't unpleasant but Susan was curious as to why he was touching her bottom. "And all men can make a milk. I'll show you how it's made."

Susan watched curiously as he rubbed his penis backwards and forwards and after a little while, white milk spurted out and he caught it in a handkerchief and showed it to her. As a family they did not 'cover up' and she had seen her father's penis many times but did not know it could make milk.

"When tha gets older, I can put myself inside thee. Ladies usually wear a cap if they don't want t' have a bairn, and take it out and douche themselves afterwards.

"Oh," said Susan, trying to understand what he meant and unsure whether as part of growing up, it was something to look forward to or not?

*Photo:* Candy, Tom, Susan and Dorothy (Calvert).

Photo: Reg, Susan (with Katy) Dorothy, Candy (with Bunny).

## 1958 MUSIC TRENDS

*"Great Balls of Fire" by Jerry Lee Lewis was one of the most outstanding "rock" numbers of 1958. The Everly Brothers had hit after hit with: "All I have to Do is Dream", "Claudette", "Bird Dog" and 'Wake up Little Susie.' The U.S.A. Army recruited Elvis and for a time he was stationed in Germany. He became a "movie" star and had hits with "Jailhouse Rock", "Hard Headed Woman," "King Creole" and "Wear My Ring Around Your Neck". Little Richard rocked with "Good Golly Miss Molly." Buddy Holly and the Crickets were surprising newcomers to the charts with "Oh Boy," "Rave On" and "Peggy Sue." Buddy proved you didn't need to be a sex idol or good looking to make it to the top. All you needed was your own original songs. Few female singers made hit records but Connie Frances did with: "Stupid Cupid," "Who's Sorry Now" and "Carolina Moon."*

*Cliff Richard was Britain's answer to Elvis. Cliff curled his lip and swung his hips as he tried to emulate Elvis. His hits included: "Move It" and "High Class Baby." Lonnie Donegan continued to skiffle and hit the charts with "The Grand Coolie Dam." Comedian, Charlie Drake made the charts with "Splish Splash". Larry Parnes moved from producing stage plays to managing attractive young boys. Marty Wilde, his new discovery, had a hit with "Endless Sleep," and Tommy Steel with "Nairobi" and "Come on Let's Go."*

# 10. BIG BEAT SPECTACULARS

By 1958, the transition to "Rock 'n' Roll" was complete. Reg had posters with "Rock n" Roll Big Beat Spectaculars" printed across the top with the names of the featured artists below. He often incorporated crazy competitions and talent shows into the evening's entertainment. In the two years since they had left Romsey, Reg had extended his circuit of dance halls widely but found it difficult to book sufficient singers and bands.

There were three 'Everly Brother' type duos in the Southampton area. The Brook Brothers, The Dowland Brothers and the Nevitt Brothers. They were all very good and Reg booked them regularly to star at his dances. Young boy bands were beginning to 'sprout' up as schoolboys across the country were learning to play guitar, many following the Bert Weedon's, 'Learn To Play In A Day' tutor. Reg auditioned any musician or group who turned up at his dances and if he liked them, offered work at his dance halls and encouraged them to rehearse and become more professional.

The 'Wranglers' were a bit different from other performers. Four apprentices earning two pounds a week each, could neither sing nor play an instrument. Miming to the latest hit records, they put together a comedy show and Reg, amused by their act, started to book them for the curtain breaks between the 'real' bands. They enjoyed working for Reg as his shows were more lively than the dances at the Pier and he picked them up in his luxurious Sheerline and transported them to various venues, these included, the British Legion Hall at Christchurch, the Drill Hall at Romsey, Empire Hall at Toton, the Lido at Winchester and Southsea Front Dance hall. At the end of the evening, he paid them one pound each.

"Would you believe it," said Reg, coming into the print room to talk to Dorothy. "I've been to Romsey and a young lad called David Hunter has put posters up all over the place saying he's going to run a Teenagers Party Night at the Crossfield Hall."
"I remember him," said Dorothy. "Dark hair and an unusual look about him. I think it's his eyes."

79

"Yes, that's him," agreed Reg.

"You have to accept that people will copy you and run dances for teenagers."

"He's got a young skiffle group together called the Four Teens. I met him and told him they wouldn't be able to dance to skiffle all night."

"Never mind," replied Dorothy.

"Can you print me some more posters for the Drill Hall?" asked Reg.

"What for?"

"I'll cover his posters with mine," said Reg with wicked smile. "It's plain daft to try and start a dance in a small town where there's one running already."

"I could do with a coffee," said Dorothy.

"I'll put the kettle on," replied Reg as he sat on the chair, watching her typeset.

"Do you think it's time for us to look for a house? We've been living here for two years now."

"I haven't time at the moment," replied Reg evasively.

"When will you have time?" asked Dorothy crossly.

"If the Rock Festival goes well, we'll have enough money to put a good deposit down on a house," replied Reg.

"What rock festival?" asked Dorothy, pausing from her work.

"I've booked the park at Eastleigh for the 19th June."

"You didn't tell me. How much will it cost?"

"Ninety pounds," replied Reg reluctantly. "It should be much bigger and better than last year. Holding it in the New Forest would have been brilliant."

Dorothy rolled her eyes in disapproval. "Except not many people had transport to get there," added Dorothy in a "told you so" voice.

"If it goes well, I should have enough to put down a good deposit on a house," smiled Reg.

"It's very risky. Have you done any proper planning and budgeting this time?"

"I'm too busy to do it now," replied Reg, standing up.

"I thought you were putting the kettle on for coffee?"

"I was."

"You can sit down for a few minutes while we go through things," said Dorothy, picking up a notepad and pen. "You have to make time. Let's work out some sums. How many bands are you booking?"

"I'm not sure yet."

"How much will they cost?" asked Dorothy.

"I don't know yet."

"What about the toilets?"

"I haven't asked," replied Reg.

"What budget have you for the stewards?"

Reg finished his cigarette and stubbed it out on the ashtray and stood up.

"Have you done any budgeting at all?" asked Dorothy, raising her voice.

"Don't get narky. It'll be fine," replied Reg.

"You could lose everything if it goes wrong and get into enormous debt," said Dorothy trying to calm her annoyance.

"Don't worry."

"I do worry," answered Dorothy. "You're not listening to me. Again."

"You always get so narky whenever I have a new idea," replied Reg irritably as he left the room. "Don't come and you won't have to worry."

Over the ensuing weeks, Dorothy continued to remind Reg to do financial planning and Reg continued to nonchalantly shrug away her suggestions. On the day of the concert, the weather was beautiful and the evening warm and balmy. Dorothy prepared her bag and packed her warmest coat and a blanket in case it was cold during the night.

"Where are you going?" asked Reg.

"To the Rock Concert of course, to be cashier," replied Dorothy.

"I don't want you there. You've done nothing but nag me about this," said Reg quietly.

"I always do the cashiering," replied Dorothy, shocked by his attitude.

"I've arranged for a steward to do it," replied Reg walking out the door. "I'll see you tomorrow."

The Rock Concert was a much bigger success than Reg could ever have expected. Teenagers danced all the night under a starry sky and twinkling lights lit up the fenced area of the park where numerous rock bands performed until the early hours of the morning. Everyone congratulated Reg on a fantastic night. In the morning, Reg returned home and undressed quietly and climbed into bed.

"How did it go," asked Dorothy yawning.

"Really well," replied Reg subdued.

"Did you have a good crowd?" asked Dorothy.

"Fantastic. They rocked all night," replied Reg, turning away.

"So what's wrong?" asked Dorothy sitting up. "Tell me Reg."

"Nothing," replied Reg.

"Don't tell me that. I can read you like a book," said Dorothy.

"If you must know, the takings were stolen," answered Reg.

"You mean the steward took them?"

"I don't know. He said someone else had taken them."

"You need to report it to the police," said Dorothy.

"What's the point?" replied Reg miserably.

"If someone's stolen money from you, you must report it."

"I've said no. I'm not going to, so don't keep going on about it," replied Reg quietly.

"You're ridiculous," retorted Dorothy angrily.

"Can you lend me some money?" asked Reg. "I've still got bills to pay and not enough dosh and everyone is expecting a bonus because it was such a good night."

"No Reg," replied Dorothy defiantly. "You wouldn't let me be cashier."

"I didn't want you to worry," replied Reg quietly.

"You were stupid and headstrong as usual and wouldn't listen to me," said Dorothy raising her voice as she got out of bed and wrapped her dressing gown around her. "You can pick up the pieces this time." Dorothy slammed the door and went downstairs to the kitchen in tears. Filling the kettle she lit the gas ring and put it on the stove and stooped down to stroke Bunny who had hopped up to her and stood on his hind legs ready for her to pick him up. "What are we going to do Bunny, he never listens to me?"

A little later, Reg, tired and weary, came down the stairs and sat with Dorothy in the dining room as she drank coffee and smoked a cigarette.

"I'm sorry," said Reg apologetically.

"You're always sorry after the event," retorted Dorothy. "You said we would only be in Portland Terrace for a few months and that was two years ago. You promised me a house with the money and the money is gone."

"I'm sorry," repeated Reg. "Do you think you can help me? Tide me over? There are quite a few people to pay."

"No," replied Dorothy bluntly. "You should go to the police."

"What's the point? They'll never find the culprit. I'll give it you back in a couple of weeks when I've earned more."

Dorothy stood up and cleared the breakfast things away. Reg followed and tried to put his arms around her.

"No Reg," said Dorothy shrugging him off. "You're pig headed and you never listen to me. And you never keep your promises."

"I promise I will."

"No," said Dorothy quietly. "I'm not helping you out this time."

Reg had always paid everyone promptly but this time, he was in debt and the various musicians and stewards all pressurised him for immediate payment and Dorothy let him squirm. Managing his accounts and doing bookwork was Reg's weak point and he decided he needed help.

"I'm going to employ a secretary," announced Reg.

"A what!" exclaimed Dorothy alarmed at the thought of her husband employing an attractive young woman.

"I've too much work and I'm having a problem keeping up. I need someone to keep accounts, pay the bills and write letters."

"It's no good asking me," replied Dorothy sharply. "I've the print works to run and I'm having a problem doing housework, washing and cooking meals."

"I've noticed," said Reg putting his hand across the table to squeeze her hand. "You need some help. You're far too intelligent to be doing housework when you can be running a successful business," smiled Reg.

"Oh yes, and what do you want, flatterer?"

"I'll ask Rita Maslin if she would like to work for us again. She was reliable in the sweet factory. She lives in Wolston. I'll pop in and ask her."

"Would you? I always liked her," agreed Dorothy.

"Why don't you have driving lessons?"

83

"I thought about it," replied Dorothy smiling.

"Would be good. You'd be able to run some of the dances."

"Oh yes, and who's going to stay in and look after the girls?"

"You could take them with you," replied Reg.

"So could you," retorted Dorothy.

"And I do need a secretary," teased Reg, watching Dorothy's expression.

"She could work in the front office," suggested Dorothy.

"I suppose she could if he were a she, but she's a man. Mr. Cole," smiled Reg. "He's nearing retirement age and he's prepared to work two or three days a week, or more, as I need him."

"Sounds good," replied Dorothy, visibly relieved.

Mr Cole, a small, well-dressed man, gave the appearance of being a gentleman's gentleman and seemed very efficient in the way he worked. Dorothy made space in the front typesetting office and Mr Cole came in three times a week to keep the books, do the banking from the dance hall takings, pay accounts and wages and send letters and telegrams to the various bands that Reg wanted to book for the dance halls. Everything seemed ordered and for the first time, proper "books" were kept.

Henry's Record shop in the St. Mary's area of Southampton kept Reg up to date with the latest releases, suggesting which ones to buy. They were about to move to larger premises further down the road.

"What's happening to this shop?" enquired Reg.

"Nothing. It'll be empty. And I think the club next door will be closing soon as well," replied the assistant.

"That's an idea," said Reg to himself and thanking the assistant, made his way home to Dorothy. He ran up the stairs, whistling, *Wake Up Little Susie*, and found Dorothy in a steamy kitchen with the twin tub turning and wet washing piled in the bath on the floor.

"Can you turn that thing off a minute?" asked Reg.

"I'm washing," replied Dorothy, drying her hands and switching the machine off. "It soon piles up. They've brought out a new machine so you don't have to do all this work putting it in one machine and then rinsing it in another and then wringing it out. It's called an automatic. You could buy me one for Christmas."

"I've had an idea," said Reg, ignoring her request. "Will you come and look at Henry's Record Shop with me?"

"What for?" asked Dorothy.

"Haven't thought yet," replied Reg casually. "The girl in the shop said the Ace of Spades Jazz Club may close. It's part of the same building and if it does, I'm thinking of taking on the lease. I could run a night club there."

"Instead of dances?"

"No. I'll still run the dances."

"Do you think it'll work? St Mary's is known for having 'queers' parading up and down the High Street on a Saturday afternoon?"

"Each to his own."

"It might put people off coming to a club," cautioned Dorothy.

"I don't think so. It didn't bother the Jazz Club. It's a very large building with loads of potential. We could run two clubs, one in the basement and one on the ground floor. And there's the shop and an office. It's got living accommodation upstairs and a flat at the back."

"I don't want to live in St Mary's."

"I wasn't thinking of us. I was thinking about the boys I'm going to manage. They will need somewhere to stay."

"Boys. What boys?" asked Dorothy alarmed.

"I need my own singers and musicians. It's hopeless relying on local bands. Most haven't got their own transport and think how often they let us down. I can't expand my areas if I haven't got my own musicians"

"Can you afford it?" asked Dorothy.

"I reckon so. At the moment I'm paying out a lot for different singers and groups, some of them not that good and the good ones, very expensive. If I have my own musicians, I can train them to perform professionally and dress them like the stars."

"What, and pay for their stage outfits?" asked Dorothy alarmed.

"Yep. And I'll need to buy dormer vans for transporting them. I thought about covering the West Country next, down to Devon. And then we could have a London tour and a northern tour."

"It's a lot to take on," cautioned Dorothy.

"It's the next step."

"You and your crazy ideas," smiled Dorothy. "You live in Cloud Cuckoo Land most of the time. You can't be in all the places at the same time. How will you manage?"

85

"I'm going to take on a road manager," replied Reg smiling. "And when you pass your test, you can run some dances for me."

David Hunter wanted to get into the entertainment business and run his own dances but he needed contacts for the bands Reg was using. He called several times at the office in Portland Terrace during his lunch breaks to ask Mr Cole to ask Reg for details with no success. On one visit, Reg came downstairs to the office wearing his tartan slippers and greeted David in a friendly manner. "Just the person I want to see," said Reg, smiling warmly as he made his way out of the front door to the car. "Hop in." David followed and got into the car. A few minutes later they were in St Mary's Street and Reg stopped outside the old Henry's Record shop.

"I've arranged a meeting to discuss taking on the lease," explained Reg. "I'm thinking of running some sort of club in the basement and a dance club in the main club area. But I need to do something with the shop? What do you think?"

"What about selling records, music and musical instruments?"

"Good idea," agreed Reg smiling. "Would you like to run it for me?"

"I'm not sure," replied David hesitating.

"I need an answer now. I'll pay you five pounds a week."

"Okay. I accept," agreed David.

The record companies refused to supply the shop so Reg arranged to purchase records on a small commission basis from Henry's and stocked the shop with various inexpensive musical instruments and sheet music. He had not lost his fascination for electrical items and bought jumbly lots cheaply at auctions and displayed them in the bottom of the window. David Hunter changed his name to Dave Jay and two girls, Janet and Donna, worked as his assistants and Mr Cole moved from Portland Terrace to the office behind the shop.

Dave Jay took a pride in keeping the shop tidy and clean. Rubbish and empty boxes were mounting up at the rear of the shop and Dave decided to have a clear out and burn the rubbish. Without thinking, he threw an empty petrol can onto the bonfire. A moment later there was a deafening blast. The can disintegrated and flew up in the air. Scorching hot ash and debris showered him and he let out a scream of excruciating pain.  His hands and face were badly burnt.  Tony Burnett, the drummer from the Hell Cats happened to be there and rushed him to the hospital on the back of his motorbike.  The burns blistered and looked ugly, taking months to heal but Dave carried on and returned to work almost immediately.

As the dance hall business expanded, Reg decided to take a gamble and train Dave to run dances, helping to load the vehicles, set up equipment on stage and announce the groups.  Dave was reserved and didn't quite fit in with the young musicians in the groups, a square peg in a round hole, but he always behaved professionally and kept his gender issues to himself.  The other boys knew he was different but they did not understand why.  In 1958, there was no information about homosexuality and relationships between consenting men were outside the law.

The shop fitting business remained a small sideline from the Romsey days and each order was a challenge to Reg's inventiveness. He received a commission to make a crystal ball for the Southampton Guildhall and constructed a large round ball in the lounge and Dorothy spent hours sticking the myriad of small square mirrors in perfect symmetry.  When complete, the ball was too wide to go through the doorway so Reg fitted a winch to the top floor window, removed the first floor window, and gingerly lowered the crystal ball to Dorothy on the pavement below.

The next day, her photograph appeared in the local newspaper as she stood on the pavement, arms outstretched to catch it.    It was delivered to the Guildhall but never fitted to the ceiling as the council engineers decided it was too heavy. Instead, it took pride of place in the ceiling of the Royal Pier Ballroom.

*Photo:* Dorothy with crystal ball. Portland Terrace.

*Photo:* Nevitt Brothers, Johnny Kidd, Dowland Brothers
(They all performed regularly at the dances).

*Photo:* Royal Pier Ballroom Teenager's Party Night c1959

# 11. THE BANDBOX

Terry Scott became a frequent visitor and friend. He, and his wife Eileen were similar ages to Reg and Dorothy, and they had a son, Terry (junior), the same age as Candy. Reg asked Terry to help him take a shop fitting display to Mays Department Store, and modestly showed him his latest invention. A large window sign of flashing lights that lit up the words, "Sleep Easy Mattresses."

"That's fantastic," laughed Terry as Reg demonstrated the sequence of flashing lights that lit up the words, "Sleep Easy Mattresses." "You're a genius. How do you think up these ideas?"
"They just come to me," laughed Reg. "How do you fancy running a nightclub for me?"
"And give up my job on the docks?" asked Terry.
"Yep. It would be full time. It's at 156 St Mary's Street."
"You mean the Ace of Spades Club?"
"Yep, that's it. I've recently taken on the lease."
"Okay, I'll ask Eileen," replied Terry, enthusiastically.
"I'm thinking of calling it the Bandbox. A club of some sort downstairs and a dance club on the ground floor."
"What about a folk club in the basement? Folk music is becoming very popular nowadays," suggested Terry.
"Could be," agreed Reg. "I hadn't thought of folk, but you're probably right. We could give it a go and see how we get on. The place is very run down. There's quite a bit of work to do."
"That's okay. I don't mind doing a bit of painting and decorating," smiled Terry.

For several weeks, everyone worked hard to transform the club and lend a hand decorating it. The whole enterprise was run on a tight budget as Reg had little spare cash. The gent's toilet did not work so the men had to use the 'ladies.' Terry organised a café on the ground floor and a folk club in the basement. The 'Teen Beat' Club was run on the ground floor and above were makeshift sleeping quarters for musicians to camp when they were on a dance hall tour, rather than pay hotel bills.

89

"Do you fancy making a name for yourself?" asked Reg, smiling mischievously.

"What do you mean?" queried Terry.

"I've had an idea."

"What sort of idea?" asked Terry catching his smile.

"If you were to stand in the front window of the music shop playing guitar on a Saturday afternoon when the High Street is busy, everyone would stop and look," grinned Reg.

"They would," agreed Terry. "But I'm not doing it Reg. I'll look an idiot."

"No you won't. It would be fun. And I'd get the press there to take your photograph. It will make the newspapers," said Reg smiling.

"I suppose it would," agreed Terry reluctantly. "It's a mad idea. Okay then. I'll give it a go."

The following week, photographs of Terry Scott playing and singing guitar in the shop window appeared in the local press, providing much needed free publicity for the shop and nightclub.

During the day, musicians often rehearsed in the basement club. Terry kept a watchful eye over the club and although quite harmless, the smoke filled atmosphere of the dark damp cellar with loud music and bodies in close proximity, became known as a 'den of iniquity.' Some teenagers were behaving oddly, as if they were drunk and Terry did not understand how they could make themselves drunk without alcohol?

"What are you drinking?" asked Terry.

"Coca Cola," came the honest reply.

"And what are you putting in it?"

"An aspirin."

With winter approaching, Reg decided to sell Brock fireworks in the shop. He ordered several hundred assorted boxes, sparklers, rockets, flying whirlwinds and many more varieties. He retained a few boxes, bangers, rockets and jumping jacks in the basement at home so he could organise a late night bonfire party. On the Saturday before 5th November, two young teenage boys came into the shop to buy some bangers. They looked so disappointed when they were told the shop had sold out that Reg took pity on them and smiling, said he would see what he could do if they would wait ten minutes. He went into the back office and mixed a concoction in empty firework tubes.

"I'm just going to test one first," said Reg as he emerged from the office with a tube.

At the rear of the shop Reg lit one of the concocted fireworks and threw it into a large municipal waste bin and stood well back. A few seconds later, there was a tremendous explosion as if a bomb had gone off and the waste bin blew up. Reg returned to the shop, red faced and grinning like a Cheshire cat. "Sorry boys, that didn't go too well. You'll have to come earlier next year to buy your fireworks."

Minutes later, the sound of fire engines and police sirens could be heard coming along the High Street towards the shop. Reg looked at Dorothy knowingly.

"I'm going to the back office, out the way."

"Oh no you're not," said Dorothy. "You can face the fireworks."

"Very funny," said Reg as the shop door opened and several police officers rushed in. Reg smiled at the officers in a friendly, apologetic manner and explained what had happened. On Monday morning, he had to report to the police station. Several hours later, he returned home, whistling, *I ain't nothing but a hound dog.*

"You sound happy," said Dorothy as he put his arms around her and gave her a kiss. "I take it you talked yourself out of trouble?"

"The Chief Constable was a Yorkshire man," replied Reg grinning and holding up the Southampton Echo.

"You jammy thing," laughed Dorothy.

"We had a lot in common and I think he could see the funny side of it. And, would you believe, the story of the exploding municipal dustbin has made the newspapers!"

On Thursday 5th November, Reg invited the musicians in the groups back to Portland Terrace after the dances. Reg paid the local neighbourhood boys to keep guard over the bonfire they had built and not to light it until eleven o clock. Dorothy cooked sausages and handed them out with bread rolls and Reg handed out fireworks. The musicians formed themselves into two gangs and prepared their positions, one side at the top of the hill and the other side at the bottom. In fun, the boys started to shoot rockets and bangers at each other. Fireworks cracked and banged, rockets whizzed in all directions. Jumping jacks were thrown at opposing sides like grenades, cracking and jumping at their opponent's feet. Everyone laughed and ran about, avoiding the fireworks aimed at them. The party was crazy and dangerous and when all the fireworks were spent, surprisingly, no one was injured and everyone asked Reg if he could organise another party next year.

Dorothy had regular driving lessons and proudly passed her driving test first time. She purchased a new, grey, Austin A35 van with the money she had saved. It was less expensive than buying a car and more practical for delivering print orders and going to the dances. She agreed to run the dance at the Drill Hall in Bournemouth and each Friday, loaded her van with loud speakers and equipment and drove with her daughters along the dark lonely roads of the New Forest to Bournemouth. Susan and Candy enjoyed going to the dances. They were allowed to dance for the first half hour and then had to stay backstage where they could watch girls in high-heeled shoes and pretty flowered dresses with skirts that flared like spinning tops as they jived and twirled, revealing layers of net petticoats and stocking tops.

Dorothy planned her journey to Huddersfield, buying numerous small gifts for her daughters and family, but this time, she would travel in her van. Her mother, Sarah Jane, had put her life savings into buying a small, two bedroom, bungalow-cottage at Nettleton Terrace in Dalton. It had no bathroom and the toilet was down the yard. The journey to reach Huddersfield took all day and it was dark when they arrived. Susan and Candy loved their visits to Huddersfield and for a few days they became an integral part of a large welcoming family.

Dorothy had written to Reg's Dad, Tom, to say she would visit with the girls and drove to Elland on her way to see her step sister, Edith and her family.

"Come on in our Dorothy, come in," said Tom smiling widely as he welcomed them into the warmth of his cottage. "Come and sit by tha fire and mak thee self at home." The girls were intrigued as they stepped over the dead dog. "Don't mind him," chuckled Tom. "He's my friend and he won't bite thee. I've bought Dundee cake and some biscuits in tha honour and I'll make thee some tea. My, how the lasses have grown."

For several hours, Dorothy chatted politely, while Tom asked questions about 'our Reggie' and what he was doing.

"I miss our Lilia. It's lonely living on your own, now our Lilia has gone," said Tom.

"I expect it is," replied Dorothy, holding her tongue and not saying what was on her mind, "You should have treated her better when she was alive."


Unlike her daughters, Dorothy disliked Huddersfield and the bleakness of the north. Each trip home reminded her how grateful she was to have escaped and moved south. Life was not perfect but as 1958 came to an end she felt an air of optimism. Post war austerity was lifting and she hoped 1959 would be the year she would have her way, and they would move to a new house. Reg however, had a different ambition. 1959 was the year he was going to recruit his own musicians.


### 1959 MUSIC TRENDS

*Elvis Presley remained 'King.' Other U.S.A. chart toppers included The Platters, The Everly Brothers, Craig Douglas, Bobby Darin, The Beverley Sisters, Ricky Nelson and Paul Anka. Buddy Holly died tragically in an air crash on 3rd February 1959 and he became an overnight, posthumous 'star.'*

*British rock 'n' roll stars were beginning to dominate U.K. charts. Cliff Richard and the Drifters had a number one with "Living Doll." Cliff's next hit, "Travellin' Light" was with his new backing group, The Shadows. Adam Faith was fortunate to be spotted by Jack Good in the 2i's Coffee Bar and asked to appear on Six Five Special on the BBC, but this did not make him a star, his first record flopped. He then worked with Roy Young, a talented young pianist and singer who suggested Adam should 'break-up' his vocals. With his 'new' voice, Adam had a chart success with "What Do You Want?" Terry Dene, also discovered in the 2i's Coffee Bar, had chart success in*

1957 and again in 1958 but lost popularity due to bad publicity for being drunk and also being discharged from the army. However, he was still a 'big' name and Reg booked him to appear at the dances.

Larry Parnes increased his 'stable' of protégé's to include Billy Fury, Vince Eager, and Joe Brown, who all appeared at Reg's dance halls. Larry signed new singers on a contract with the promise of a weekly wage but he was renowned for being tight with money and retaining record royalties and other earnings. Marty Wilde's hits included "A Teenager in Love", "Donna" and "Sea of Love".

The BBC recognised for the first time a teenage pop culture and devoted (only) half an hour a week to pop music on Saturday nights. The programme was called "Six Five Special." The producer, Jack Good, migrated to the more progressive ITV and produced "Oh Boy," and invited his favoured "stars" to perform as celebrity guests.

*Photo:* c 1960 Billy Fury pulling a pint at the Seven Stars, Rugby. He was booked to star at the dance halls and the Seven Stars was where the 'boys' stayed when on tour in the Midlands. The boys believed the pub was haunted and had some strange nightly experiences!

# 12. THE BANDBOX BOYS

Reg learnt step by step, mistake by mistake, how to run a business. Expanding so rapidly meant doing "sums" on the inside of cigarette packets and envelopes. Having a secretary was a big help but he still did the mental arithmetic to ensure he was earning enough to pay rent for the Bandbox and Portland Terrace, hiring the dance halls, money for musicians, cloakroom ladies, cashiers, stewards, petrol, posters, adverts, tickets, wages for Mr Cole, Terry Scott, Dave Jay, Donna and Janet and his new road manager, Chris Lawton. Outwardly, he seemed to be earning large sums of money and he was generous with the people he employed, but with Dorothy, he expected her to be financially self-sufficient.

"Mr Cole is going to have a two week holiday," said Reg. "Do you think you could help with paying the wages while he's away?"

"Yes, if you like," replied Dorothy. "I'll come down to the office on Friday morning."

"Thanks Doe Doe," said Reg, giving her a hug and kiss.

Dorothy worked out the wages and put the money into small brown envelopes. Out of curiosity, she decided to look over the books to check what was going on. Dorothy was good at accounts and quickly worked out the sums. When Reg returned to the office, Dorothy took him by surprise.

"I've been looking over the accounts and checking the figures," explained Dorothy.

"Mr Cole's very good," said Reg casually.

"Yes he is, but not in the way you think."

"What do you mean?" asked Reg, looking concerned.

"From what I can see, he's cooking the books. They don't add up," said Dorothy raising her eyebrows.

"Don't add up! I thought he was as straight as a pole," exclaimed Reg, shocked.

"I've done a quick summary and I think he's embezzled about a thousand pounds since he's been working for you."

"He couldn't have done. I would have sworn he was honest."

"You can never tell," replied Dorothy. "Come and look at the figures, I'll show you."

"No, I believe you."

"You'll have to go to the police."

"I don't want to do that," replied Reg quietly.

"Why not? He's been dishonest. He should go to prison for what he's done, or at least pay back what he's stolen."

"I'll give him the sack. We can write to him and tell him we no longer require his services."

"You should report him to the police," insisted Dorothy.

"I'm not going to and that's the end of the matter," replied Reg forcefully. "I'm giving him the sack."

Mr Stennings was employed as the new secretary, a man in his fifties, portly and balding. He was another gentleman's gentleman with a partiality for young, good-looking boys.

Reg expanded his area towards London and booked a beautiful ballroom, the Strava in Islington on Sunday evenings. Rory Blackwell was in residency. Although he had no hit records, he was famous as the first rock 'n' roller in Britain and performed on television in "Oh Boy" and "Six Five Special." When Bill Haley arrived in England at Southampton docks, Rory was there to greet him, playing drums and singing with his band, The Blackjacks.

Dorothy, Terry Scott and Eileen often accompanied Reg for a social and working night out at the Strava, the two ladies acting as cashiers. When Reg and Terry had set up the equipment, they liked to relax before the start of the show. One night, they were surprised as the front doors were pushed open and a gang of armed men ran into the hall. It was like an American movie but it was happening before their eyes. The armed men shouted for everyone to get down and then they started to fire at the mirrored screen behind the bar.

"Get down," shouted Reg to Dorothy who stood frozen to the spot. He grabbed her and pulled her down as guns fired and cracked and shattered mirror glass flew everywhere, splintering into shards that danced on the ballroom floor. The men reached for the till behind the bar, grabbed the money and ran out of the hall, pulling out the telephone wires as they departed. Within two minutes, they were gone, slamming the doors behind them as they made a speedy exit to a waiting car and drove off at full speed.

It was enough for Reg and Dorothy. The dances at the Islington Strava were brought to an end and Rory Blackwell decided to move on and accept a safer residency, a summer season at Butlins in Wales.

Reg was like the Pied Piper, attracting young musicians to his 'cave.' He went to the 2i's coffee bar in Soho, ran talent competitions at the dances and looked for local groups who had potential to go professional. He offered them all a regular weekly wage, usually double what they were earning in their normal job, and free accommodation. They followed him happily and became known locally as 'The Bandbox Boys.' Reg and Dorothy always referred to them as 'the boys,' regardless of their age and to the younger ones, they became like second parents.

Four young apprentices, cocky with attitude, earning two pounds a week each, began to practice playing rock 'n' roll. They called themselves the 'Hell Cats.' Colin Wilsher, aged seventeen, was lead singer and guitarist. A good looking boy with a mass of light brown hair combed back; he had given himself the unlikely stage name of Colin Angel. He was accompanied by Tony Burnett on drums and Pete Mist on bass. The three were employed as apprentices at Kennedy's Builders Merchants in Southampton. The fourth member, Jeff Chalke, played rhythm guitar and worked at Thorneycroft's Shipbuilders Yard. Jeff hated it. Thorneycroft's employed many apprentices on cheap wages and had a reputation for making most of them redundant when they reached the age of twenty-one.

The Hell Cats played their first gig at the pier for Len Canham and then asked for an audition with Reg. They had no transport so Reg took them to the dance at the Lymington Masonic Hall. They were impressed by being picked up in his luxurious big limousine and to their surprise, at the end of the show, Reg offered them a permanent job earning three pounds ten shillings a week each.

"I've just started a West Country circuit with dance halls at Salisbury, Exmouth, Exeter, Torquay and Weymouth," explained Reg. "If you can start straight away, you can go on tour from tomorrow."

The four boys were so excited to be asked to become professional rock 'n' roll musicians that they managed to persuade their parents to let them leave their apprenticeships. The following day, they all arrived at the Bandbox and Reg was pleased to see them. He suggested they change their name to "Colin Angel and the Choir Boys," and they agreed. They were young and inexperienced but keen to learn. Within a short time they were packed into a van, ready to begin their new lives.

Reg had bought a second-hand Dormer van and a Comma van with no seats. He found old cinema seats and placed them on the floor for the musicians to sit on, in between guitars, loud speakers and drum kit. New record releases were provided for the musicians to learn as no one could read music the boys taught them-selves to play 'by ear,' listening, over and over to the records, copying the chord changes and writing down lyrics. To make his protégé's stand out, Reg bought amazing stage outfits, gold and silver lamé jackets, satin jackets, colourful suits and shirts. When the boys appeared on the stage, they immediately looked like stars and with practice and rehearsal they began to perform better than most of the famous stars they copied.

Dave Da Costa, older than the other boys, aged twenty-two and married, could sing and play lead guitar. Reg recruited him because he was a qualified driver and could drive a van to the dance halls. A natural comedian, he larked about and did extreme things, often in very bad taste. His light brown hair was fixed permanently into a Tony Curtis hairstyle. He moved into the top floor of the end Portland Terrace house, with his wife, Debbie, who was by contrast, quiet and shy.

When Dave Da Costa was a passenger in the van he liked to shock pedestrians by poking his bare posterior outside the van window. One day, instead of walking down three flights of stairs to the toilet, he put his posterior outside the top front window and did his ablutions. His faeces plopped onto the pavement below, next to Candy who promptly ran in to tell her mother. Reg was furious. This was unacceptable behaviour and Reg duly told Dave, not to do it again.

At the end of each show it was normal for the boys to "dally" and enjoy the perks of being a star with star-struck girls. If they were too long, the van would leave without them and they had to make their own way home. As Dave was usually the driver he often kept the band waiting a very long time!

Reg had taken a liking to a singer called Carol Laine from the first time he saw her play with the Ray Waller Townsmen. Carol, now aged nineteen, suffered with stage nerves and was often sick before each performance. She looked a lot like Dorothy and lived with her parents in Eastleigh.

"I don't know why you've employed her," said Dorothy. "She's quite nice but she's not that good. She doesn't have a lot about her."

"We need a girl singer. We have to appeal to the boys in the audience as well as the girls."

"I suppose," agreed Dorothy reluctantly. "But you could look for a better singer."

"Maybe," replied Reg evasively.

Reg continued to expand his network of dance halls from the south coast up to outer London. On Monday nights he went to Staines Town Hall, often with Dorothy as cashier.

"Mrs Maslin can't baby-sit on Monday night, so you'll need to ask someone else to be cashier," said Dorothy.

"Pity. I'll have to ask Dave Jay. I've booked Cliff Bennett and the Rebel Rousers. Should be a good show."

"Cliff's a bit wooden, but he sings well enough," commented Dorothy.

"He brought a young boy with him last time, he's got real charisma and the girls went mad for him. I tried to get him to work for me but he wasn't sure so I'm going to ask him again tonight."

"So if you're late I'll know you'll be talking to his parents," smiled Dorothy knowingly.

David Hurran was undoubtedly one of the best looking boys with potential Reg had seen. He observed him carefully as he sang several rock numbers with the Rebel Rousers and when the interval came, Reg smiling warmly, led the boy off the stage to talk in privacy.

"I think you could be a professional singer," said Reg.

"I don't think so," replied David modestly. "I just enjoy getting up with the band and doing a few numbers."

"How old are you?" asked Reg.

"Sixteen."

"I've a vacancy for a singer to join the shows I put on. You would have your own backing group," said Reg pausing, allowing David to consider the proposal.

"I've just started my apprenticeship."

"I'll pay you more than double what you'll earn as an apprentice with increases as you improve. You'll earn a lot more as a singer than doing anything else."

"I'm not sure," hesitated David.

"I can take you home after the show and we can talk to your parents. It's up to you."

"Okay. I can ask them," agreed David, hesitating. "They probably won't agree."

"That's fine," smiled Reg amiably. "Meet me backstage at the end of the show and I'll drive you home."


Over cups of tea and cake, Reg spent several hours talking to Mr and Mrs Hurran and eventually persuaded them to allow David to join him the following week. With great excitement and apprehension, David travelled down to Southampton to begin his life as a rock 'n' roll singer. He moved into the Bandbox for a short time until Tony Burnett's mother took pity on him and offered him lodgings at her house.


Few people in the entertainment business kept their own name and naming a new singer became a group event with everyone making suggestions. Reg rewarded the person who thought of the 'winning' name with a pound note and with much fun and laughter, everyone called out suggestions for the new recruit. After much deliberation, David Hurran became "Danny Storm."

"I think you might look like Cliff Richard if we dyed your hair black."

"Do you think so?" asked Danny shyly.

"I'll take you to the barbers and pick you up later," said Reg, steering Danny to his car. When they reached the barbers, Reg instructed the barber, "To make his hair as black as possible." Two hours later, the change in Danny's appearance was remarkable.

"Wow. Meet the new Cliff Richard," said Reg grinning. "What do you think? Do you like your new look?"

"It's all right," agreed Danny smiling.

"The next stop is to get you measured for a white stage suit and find white shoes to match," said Reg happily. He was really pleased with his new recruit.

Colin Angel and the Choir Boys were to become Danny's new backing group. Reg bought them a second stage outfit and in the record break they changed their appearance and became "The Strollers." For several weeks, they rehearsed with Danny, learning more and more new songs, synchronizing their movements as they sang and played. Reg showed Danny how he wanted him to move. He was a natural and easily swung his hips. Finally, to improve Danny's singing voice and breathing, he was booked for ten singing lessons with Madam Argenti.

When the initial training period was over Dorothy printed posters with a photo of Danny in silhouette. Under the photograph was printed, "Mystery Singer will appear at (whatever dance hall) and the date." The silhouette posters were displayed and attracted large audiences and Danny caused a "storm" wherever he performed. It took the girls a little while to realise it wasn't actually Cliff Richard but they didn't mind. He was, in their eyes, just as good and they screamed and tried to pull him off the stage. Boyfriends resented Danny and to keep the equilibrium Carol Laine would often appear on the same show. Invariably, where Carol was, Reg was too.

The 'real' Cliff Richard was doing a show at the Gaumont and it seemed as if all the teenage girls in Southampton were queuing up to see him.  Reg arranged to pick Danny up from his lodgings, and, in mischievous mood whistled as he drove to the front of the Gaumont. Reg slowed the car down and said to Danny with a big grin, "When I say jump, jump, and run for your life."  Danny, surprised, followed Reg's instructions.  To his utter amazement, as soon as the girls saw him they screamed and started to chase after him.  They had mistaken Danny for Cliff.  Danny ran.  He had to run for his life as the screaming mob closed in on him.  Just in time, Reg drove the car round and rescued him.  In the following day's newspaper was the story of Danny Storm and the mistaken identity.

Vince Taylor had been discovered at the 2i's Coffee Bar in Soho and Jack Good, the producer of 'Oh Boy,' invited him to appear on his television shows but wanted him to look 'respectable' and have his hair cut short.  Vince refused so his television appearances were cut short!  Vince emulated both Elvis and Gene Vincent, with black hair and wearing black leathers.  He was famous and out of work so Reg booked him to do a tour of the dance halls in the autumn of 1959.  He needed a backing group so Reg needed to find more musicians to make up 'The Playboys.'  He decided to put together bass guitarist Johnny Vance and drummer, Johnny Watson, but he still needed a lead guitarist.

Reg went to the 2i's to look for a lead guitarist with Vince and noticed a very tall young man with dark hair playing guitar.  Reg made his way over and asked, "Have you thought about becoming professional?"

"Not really, I just enjoy playing," confessed the tall young man.

"I need a lead guitarist.  I'm putting together 'The Playboys' for Vince Taylor.  He's going to do an autumn tour of my dance halls."

"Oh," said the surprised young man.  Everyone had heard of Vince Taylor.

"Would you like the job?"

"I'm not sure," hesitated the young man.  "I'll need to talk to my parents."

"I have to have someone start the tour tomorrow so you would need to travel back with me tonight to Southampton."

"My parents are expecting me home tonight."

"Can you telephone them?" asked Reg.

"No, they don't have a "phone."

"Ah. Then you'll have to decide," said Reg.

"I'll do it," replied the young man impulsively.

"What's your name?" asked Reg as they shook hands.

"Geoffrey Glover-Wright."

Reg returned Geoffrey to his parent's home in North London a few days later. To say they were angry would be an understatement, they had been worried and were furious. Reg was both apologetic and persuasive. He spent time talking to them until they eventually capitulated. They wanted Geoffrey to train as a barrister but could see he had made his mind up to become a musician. Public school educated, Geoffrey stood out from the other boys and had an almost aristocratic air about him. It was clear he was ambitious and more calculating than most, but even so he accepted life as a musician without complaint and relished the experience.

Martin Upperdine and Don Ker both aged nineteen, decided like Dick Whittington, to move from Coventry and try their luck in London. They went to see the Vince Taylor show at Battersea Town Hall and at the end of the evening, dallied in the bar. They recognised Geoffrey when he came in for a drink and the two boys took their opportunity to chat to him, and explain, they were musicians looking for work.

"Why don't you come and see my boss?" suggested Geoffrey. "Come on up to the dressing room, I'll introduce you."

"Are you sure he won't mind?" asked Johnny.

"No, he'll be fine. He always listens to new people."

Reg smiled and greeted the two boys amiably. Martin had recently dyed his hair bright blond, Jeff's hair was naturally black. They looked good but Reg needed to hear them.

"The p.a. system is turned off so you'll have to play without amplification," said Reg as he led the boys down to the dimly lit stage. "Do something to impress me."

The two boys stood on stage looking at each other. This was their big chance. Don borrowed a guitar and they played and sang with no amplification as best they could in front of an audience of one.

"Good, very good. I like the way you move," said Reg to Martin. "Let me have your contact details and I may be in touch in the New Year if we have an opening. It would mean moving to Southampton."

"That'd be okay," agreed Martin and Don, feeling chuffed.

As the number of Reg's protégé's grew, he decided he needed somewhere better for them to stay and he looked around for another house to rent.

"I need more accommodation for the boys," said Reg casually over breakfast.

"What about more accommodation for us? When are you going to think about us Reg?"

"I've seen a house in Derby Road. It's quite a substantial Victorian terraced house," replied Reg, ignoring her quip and passing over some property details.

"Derby Road, isn't that the red light district?" asked Dorothy.

"Probably," replied Reg with a big grin. "But I don't suppose the boys will mind."

"Really," said Dorothy sarcastically.

"I do need more accommodation."

"I agree. It's not a good environment for young boys to live above the Bandbox," replied Dorothy looking through the particulars. "The house looks okay."

"You can come and have a look, help me to furnish it."

"As if I haven't enough to do," retorted Dorothy, although she was pleased to be asked.

"And I've another idea," said Reg, as he began to stir the sugar round and round in he sugar bowl. "What do you think about me linking up with the 2i's coffee bar in London?"

"How?" asked Dorothy sceptically as she buttered toast and removed the sugar bowl.

"Not sure yet," replied Reg. "I'm thinking about it. Some sort of television receiver or radio link."

"I expect it will be illegal," replied Dorothy. "Do you want coffee or tea?"

"Coffee please, I'm going to have a meeting with Paul Lincoln at the 2i's and discuss it," said Reg with enthusiasm. "We could do a link through to our basement club with their club and connect Southampton stars with the London stars.

"Yeah, yeah, yeah," replied Dorothy. "Pigs can fly."

"Anything is possible," replied Reg determinedly.

"Yes. Anything is. Do you think it's possible for you to make time for us to go house hunting for us?" asked Dorothy.

"Not this week, I've too much on."

"As always," replied Dorothy irritably.

Dorothy helped Reg to furnish the Derby Road house and the accommodation proved more comfortable than the Portland Terrace house. The 'ladies' of the red light district were kindly neighbours, taking on a platonic, motherly role, making cups of tea and providing the occasional home cooked meals.

Reg had developed his own way of putting on a show quite different from anyone else, with various lead singers all sharing the same backing group. Reg looked for hidden talent and encouraged comedy and humour into the acts. The protocol at dance halls was for his boys to behave like 'stars' and remain back stage, not even to go to the toilet in the hall. They had to retain a mystery like gods to the awestruck girls. None of the dance halls had alcohol licences and both Reg and Dorothy were virtually teetotal. Reg was totally against his musicians drinking alcohol while they were working, and insisted alcohol would not improve their performance.

Len Canham had followed Reg's lead and introduced 'Teenage Party Nights' at the Pier on Wednesday and Saturday evenings. The two men remained friends and often exchanged acts. Len had his own entourage of young men including Tex Roburg, the Brook Brothers, The Strangers, The Blackjacks and The Dominoes. Bob Potter was another who decided to copy Reg and started to run teenage dances towards London. Territorial boundaries were crossed and both Bob Potter and Reg became defensive. It was not feasible to have two dance halls being run on the same night, in the same area. In competition, both party's played annoying, dirty tricks by sticking 'cancelled' on their rivals posters and putting sugar in the petrol tanks of their vehicles to cause havoc on their late night journeys home!

*Photo (top)*:
Camping in New Forest.
Dave Jay (on roof). Reg,
Baby Bubbly,
Carol Laine,
Danny Storm,
Eddie Sex,
Dave Da Costa.

(*Left*): Bedroom in Derby Road House.
*(standing)*
Dave Da Costa,
Baby Bubbly,
Danny Storm.
*(on bed)*
Ricky Fever,
Glen Dale.

*Photo (right)*:
Danny Storm
and
Eddie Sex,
probably at
Staines Town
Hall or Lye.

*(Below):*
BIG BEAT
POSTER
(approx 6 feet
wide printed in
bright colours.)
(JM)

*Photo (top):* Loading the vans. Reg, Dave Da Costa, Danny Storm, Ricky Fever, Dave Jay (on roof), Baby Bubbly, Eddie Sex.
*Photo (bottom left)*: Johnny Martin with Don Ker playing guitar. (JM)
*Photo (bottom right)*: Danny Storm, Pete Mist playing guitar.

Photo (Top left):
Danny Storm and Eddie Sex.

(Right): Jeff Chalke (JM)

(Bottom): Rory Blackwell behind
the Bandbox, on a carnival float,
Southampton. (JM)

*Photo (left):*
Dave Da Costa,
a natural comedian
always larking about,
often in bad taste.

*Photo (below):*
Reg combing Danny
Storm's hair for
publicity picture.
Dave Da Costa and
Glen Dale watching.

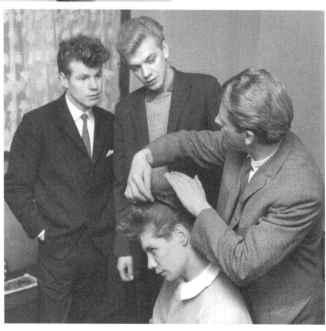

# 13. FAMILY MATTERS

"You're nothing but a hound dog," sang Reg as he ran up the stairs to see Dorothy.

"Why are you singing?" asked Dorothy as she stood at the gas cooker, stirring the gravy pan.

"Why not," replied Reg looking over her shoulder and putting his arms about her waist.

"Come off, or your dinner will be rabbit's dinner on the floor," said Dorothy smiling. She was happy when Reg was happy.

"It could be dinner for the dog," teased Reg.

"Can you open that tin of corned beef?" Dorothy asked pointing with her head.

"I've met someone who knows where a Pyrenean Mountain Dog needs a home."

"A what?"

"A big white dog," replied Reg smiling. "What do you think girls? Do you want to come and have a look at a dog this evening?" he asked, poking his head round the kitchen door to the dining area where Susan and Candy were waiting for their meal.

"You shouldn't get them excited. What if we don't like it?" asked Dorothy stirring the corned beef into a pan of boiled potatoes, carrots, onions and gravy.

"It's got eczema but nothing else wrong with it. The previous owners starved it. If the breeders can't find him a good home they're going to have him put down."

"I can't understand how people can be so cruel," said Dorothy serving up the steaming corned beef hash onto four plates.

Major was perfectly behaved, he moved quietly behind his owners and greeted the visitors shyly, however, after a moment, he was wagging his tail and enjoying the fuss everyone made of him. It was love at first sight.

"He's beautiful," said Susan stroking his forehead. "Can we keep him?"

Reg glanced at Dorothy for her confirmation.

"Yes, we'll keep him," replied Reg. "It looks as though he needs lots of loving."

When they arrived home Major was introduced first to Katy. Susan held her cat in her arms while Reg held Major's collar as he brought him into the room. Katy sprang off Susan, hissed, arched her back and fluffed out her fur. Major retreated submissively but as he became more confident and approached Katy, she retaliated and smacked his nose with her claws extended and snootily walked away.

"That's fine," laughed Dorothy. "Katy's in charge, cats usually dominate a dog. Let's see how he does with Bunny."

Major was more curious to see a rabbit in the kitchen. Reg held even tighter to his collar as Bunny, with no fear, hopped towards Major and kept sniffing and twitching his nose. Major sniffed back. Bunny stamped his feet, hammering like a drum to let Major know that the kitchen was his domain. Major shook his head so his ears flapped and Bunny hopped away and sat in his box.

"I think they might become friends," said Dorothy. "Major seems very gentle. Perhaps the things they said about him being fierce are exaggerated."

Dorothy loved to have breakfast in bed so Reg offered his daughters pocket money in exchange for making it. Two slices of white bread, toasted one side and buttered, and instant coffee made with milk and two teaspoons of sugar. Carefully, they carried this up to their parents bedroom before they left for school and Dorothy gave them their bus fares and a kiss.

On the first morning of Major's arrival, the girls got up early to play with him and then made their mother's breakfast and left for school. A little later, Rita Maslin let herself in and went upstairs to clean. As she entered the lounge, Major pounced on her knocking her flat on the floor. Hearing screams and Major's angry growls, Dorothy and Reg jumped out of bed and ran downstairs. Reg immediately pulled the dog off and Dorothy helped Mrs. Maslin to her feet. Once they had settled down and given Mrs Maslin a cup of tea, they introduced Major to her properly, but he was having none of it. She was an intruder and he refused to accept her into his household. From that day on he had to be tied to the piano leg in the lounge whenever she came in to clean.

Major proved a wonderful, but untrustworthy pet. He was gentle and well behaved with his family but not with strangers. After the dances, Dorothy and Reg took him for a walk in the deserted parks close to their home and allowed him freedom to gallop through the trees as they played ball with him. One night, an unsuspecting cyclist, whistling and wheeling along the dark pathway between the trees caught Major's attention and a chase ensued. Reg kept shouting at the man to get off his bike and hold it up like a shield. The man ignored him not understanding what Reg meant until he saw Major about to pounce. The startled man almost fell off his bike and did as he was instructed. Out of breath Reg reached Major and caught him. As soon as he did, Major became calm and gentle. The man, cursing profusely, continued on his journey.

Similar events became a regular occurrence. He attacked a refuse collector and it cost Reg five pounds for a new jacket. Only Reg was strong enough to take him for walks and they could not let him off the lead.

Dorothy took Major to St Mary's High Street and left him in the van with the window slightly open while she went into the Bandbox. Major put his paw on the window, pulled it down and made his escape. Within minutes, people were running and screaming into shops for safety. The police received a number of calls and were speeding to the area. Dorothy, oblivious, returned to the van and was surprised to see the deserted street on a normally brimming Saturday afternoon. Getting into the van and realising Major was not there, she quickly assessed the situation. Running up and down the high street calling his name, she found him in a shop doorway with his teeth barred and growling. As she approached, he changed character and came back to her as good and meek as a friendly lion.

For four months Reg and Dorothy did their best to calm Major but his mood swings were unpredictable and they had no choice but to reluctantly return him to the breeders.

As time passed Reg realised Dorothy was his best business asset. He encouraged her to run more dances and she sometimes acted as cashier to ensure the honesty of the regular cashier, as they could see if Dorothy's takings were markedly different to theirs and at the same time, she was able to pay herself a wage. Susan was trusted by her parents to look after her younger sister when they were out at night, with strict instructions for them both to be in bed by eight pm.

Dorothy could not help suggesting to Reg ways he could consolidate and manage his business more efficiently and this was an irritation to him. They were both stubborn and when Reg refused to listen to her advice, it infuriated her. He had so many ideas spinning around in his head, people to see and new things to try, he did not want to consolidate or have his wings clipped. Reg thrived on excitement whilst Dorothy longed for stability, order and routine. In frustration, she began to shout. With other people, Dorothy was quiet and shy but at home, she shouted at Reg, shouted at her children and shouted more often than she spoke. And she worried. As soon as Reg succeeded to make one project work, he lost interest and moved onto the next.

Reg and Dorothy loved and laughed but argued more and more. There were days when Dorothy became depressed, never seeing an end to her problem of living with Reg and criticised him continually, pouring out her pent-up emotions to her sensitive, eleven year old daughter. Susan listened, saying little, except to comfort her mother when she burst out crying. Susan adored her father and could not comprehend her mother's unhappiness. If the child said one word in favour of her father, Dorothy snapped and shouted at her. "You always stick up for your Dad. But it's me who scrimped and saved to bring you up, not your father."

Candy, aged nine, seemed oblivious to most of what was going on and Dorothy was kinder and more protective of her youngest daughter. Susan began to suffer terrible stomach pains and in her dreams, imagined her mother was trying to poison her. It became so severe that the doctor diagnosed her suffering from a suspected stomach ulcer and suggested Dorothy should take her to see a child psychiatrist to help her troubled mind, but Dorothy rejected this suggestion.

Rita Maslin, was by contrast, warm and homely with endless patience and never raised her voice. She was content with her life and continually praised her own children, Maureen and Bobby, proudly recounting each small achievement they made.

"Why does Mrs Maslin always praise her children and never say anything bad about them?" asked Susan. She may well have asked why the moon was in the sky and why the world rotated around the sun?

"Does she?" replied Dorothy, surprised by the question.

"Why do you never say anything good about me? Or Candy?" persisted Susan. She wanted to ask her mother why she never said anything good about anyone, but realised this was one question too far.

"You should never praise your own children," replied Dorothy.

"Why?" asked Susan.

"It makes them big headed," replied Dorothy tartly, trying to end the conversation.

"Are Bobby and Maureen big headed?" persisted Susan.

"No, but they could be. It's not right for mothers to boast about their children as if they were perfect and the best in the world."

Reg loved fairgrounds and when the fair came to Southampton Common he would happily take Dorothy and his daughters for an evening out. He was familiar with many of the fairground characters as they remembered him from the days he had sold popcorn and toffee apples. Reg gave his daughters money to choose their rides and when they had finished, they had a dodgem car fight, Dorothy with Candy in one car and Reg with Susan in another. They chased each other round the rink laughing and screaming as they bumped each other as hard as they could. He then bought everyone a large pink candy-floss. Dorothy did not like the fast rides and preferred to stand and watch.

"Why don't you have a go on the big wheel? It's slow and safe," suggested Reg.

Dorothy agreed and Reg stayed on the ground and watched his family go up, higher and higher in the air and started a conversation with the man in control of the wheel. Each time Dorothy's chair touched the ground it would swing on round and they had another turn. After two slow rotations they were all getting bored. By the third Dorothy was becoming angry. By the fourth she was furious. Reg waved and grinned at her while he talked to the man. Dorothy pulled faces, scowled, shouted, called and beckoned to be let out but to no avail. The wheel just kept going round and round. Eventually, the car bumped to a stop and they were helped out. Dorothy bit her lip and stared angrily at Reg while he laughed at her.

"That wasn't funny," she hissed. "Little things please little minds."

The results of the eleven plus exam came through. Dorothy was mortified and ashamed she had produced a child who was not clever enough to go to a grammar school as she had done so effortlessly. Years of moving from school to school, being the youngest in the class or receiving a poor education was no reason for failure. "I expect Candy will pass the exam," said Dorothy as she read the note.

Towards the end of the summer, Dorothy went shopping and returned with bags containing navy blue school uniform. "I've managed to get you a place at Regent's Park School," said Dorothy smiling. "Come and try your uniform on." It was a special occasion to have new clothes and Susan was excited and happy. First she tried on the skirt. It was too long, nearly reaching her ankles.

"I know it's big," said Dorothy. "I can't afford to buy you a new skirt every year."

"I look awful," said Susan as she tried to roll up the skirt around the waistband.

"Stop it," said Dorothy crossly. "You'll spoil the shape of the pleats. You'll grow into it soon enough."

"This blouse is too big," commented Susan miserably.

"I told you, it has to last," snapped Dorothy.

"The sleeves are over my finger tips," said Susan holding her arms down and hiding her hands.

"I can make the button tighter to keep them up," replied Dorothy as she passed the cardigan. Dorothy had been knitting the cardigan all summer and it had not worked out successfully. Everything was a misfit. The sleeves were baggy and the body of the cardigan was made for a small fat girl. "You must have grown taller," exclaimed Dorothy, disappointed. "Stop pulling it down or you'll spoil it. It's taken me months to knit. Now try the coat."

"It's old," exclaimed Susan.

"It's not that old and I've had it dry cleaned," replied Dorothy helping her to put it on.

"Someone has had it first," said Susan dismayed and fidgeting about, looking at her reflection in the mirror. "It's too long and the belt's missing."

"It looks better without the belt."

"There are holes in the pockets," said Susan pulling out the pockets and showing her mother the holes.

"Never mind. Just don't put anything in them,"

Reg never interfered in the way Dorothy brought up their daughters but music was something he did care about and he wanted his daughters to have the best.

"I've booked the girls to start lessons on Saturday morning. One hour each."

"Oh," said Dorothy surprised. "I thought they were doing okay learning from the tutor."

"They'll do better if they had a proper piano teacher," insisted Reg.

"How much will it cost?" asked Dorothy.

"Seven shillings and six pence an hour, each," replied Reg.

"Fifteen shillings a week," said Dorothy shocked. "That's a lot of money to spend on piano lessons."

"He's a good pianist and if they're going to learn they need the best," insisted Reg.

"Candy's the one with the musical ear," said Dorothy. "I suppose it might be worth it for her."

"And Susan's the one who practices," said Reg. "She's always playing the piano and teaching herself new pieces."

"She doesn't have a musical ear."

"You don't need one if you love playing," replied Reg.

"I think it's a waste of money if you haven't a musical ear."

"I'll walk them there on Saturday so that they know where to go."

"Just so long as you pay," remarked Dorothy. She could not help her nature. She disliked paying for anything out of the ordinary and did not believe in spoiling her children.

The annual fair returned to Southampton Common in the autumn and the girls begged their father to take them.

"I'm sorry," Reg replied. "I'm too busy this year."

"Oh Dad," complained Susan, giving her Dad a cuddle as he put his arms out to embrace both of his daughters. .

"I really can't. You could ask your Mum," Reg replied looking across at Dorothy who grimaced her response.

"You know I don't like fairgrounds. That's your job to take them to the fair," said Dorothy.

"I'll tell you what," Reg replied, putting his hand in his pocket. "Here's ten shillings. That's five shillings each for rides. I'm sure you're old enough to go to the fair on your own."

"Thanks Dad," responded both the girls, giving him a big hug.

Susan and Candy walked to the Common, both girls wrapped warm in their school coats. They were excited about being allowed out at night on their own. This was the first time and as they were walking round the fairground, a very nice man started to chat to them and ask them where they were from. The girls had been brought up to be polite and Susan answered his questions vaguely. They spent time choosing their rides and argued about who was going to drive the dodgem car. When their money was spent the girls wandered aimlessly, watching the rides.

"Would you like another ride?" asked the man as he gave them some money. The two girls refused politely but he insisted. "Go on. It's all right. Have another ride." The man, smiling as he watched, waved at the girls as they went round and round and up and down on the merry go round. When the ride came to an end, he began to walk round with them and thrust his hand into Susan's coat pocket. His fingers found the hole in the pocket and he worked his fingers round and started to touch her. Susan did not know what to do. He stayed right next to her and kept feeling her as they walked. It wasn't unpleasant but Susan was very uneasy about being touched and instinctively knew it was wrong.

"Would you like a Candy Floss," he asked.

"Yes please," responded Candy immediately.

Susan tried to walk faster than the man, but he was there, with her, with his hand in her pocket. She was puzzled as to why he was

118

feeling her. He took his hand out to buy the Candy Floss and Susan took her opportunity.

"Thank you very much," she said, not looking at him. "But we've got to go home. We've been told not to be late."

"Thank you," responded Candy.

Both the girls waved at him and he waved back as they darted off.

The ghost of the house continued to walk when they forgot to close the door to the cellar and there were strange noises, scratching and running about in the night. Dorothy awoke and nudged Reg.

"I think we've got mice," said Dorothy.

"Sounds more like elephants to me," replied Reg sleepily.

"It might be rats. What do you think?" asked Dorothy.

"Go to sleep, I'll buy some rat poison tomorrow," replied Reg turning over.

The following day, rat poison was placed in various corners of the house but they forgot Bunny was a rodent. He ate the poisoned oats and became seriously ill. Dorothy nursed him and he recovered slowly. And then he died. Susan found him stretched out as if sleeping on the kitchen floor. Sobbing, she ran to her mother in the print works. Dorothy hugged her and they cried together. He had been the most wonderful rabbit, a real character in the family.

As Christmas drew closer, Reg started to think about the shows and dances and planned to open Bandbox on Boxing Day.

"Hi Terry, I've been looking for you," smiled Reg as Terry came in with a large box.

"I've been shopping," replied Terry grinning as he put the box down on the floor.

"Shopping for Christmas?" asked Reg.

"No. A new tea urn, the old one burnt out," replied Terry as he began to install it.

"I wanted to see you about Boxing Day."

"What about Boxing Day?" asked Terry.

"I thought we'd organise a Boxing night party in the club. It should go well as nothing else is open."

"Sorry. No can do," replied Terry. "I've planned Christmas and Boxing day with my family."

"Work has to come first," responded Reg.

"Not over Christmas it doesn't," replied Terry affably. "My family comes first."

"Dorothy and the girls are going to Huddersfield," said Reg.

"That's okay for you then, but I have to be with my family," replied Terry firmly as he assembled the tea urn.

"I really do want to open Boxing night. It would be good for the club. We'd attract some new members."

"I'm sorry Reg. My family come first. I can't do it."

"That's difficult," replied Reg slowly.

"You'll have to find someone else to run it for you," suggested Terry.

"There is no one else. We're all out working Boxing night. It's one of the main nights of the year."

"Not for me, Eileen wouldn't speak to me if I went out Boxing night," said Terry as he lifted the urn onto the counter and started to fit it into position.

"Are you handing in your notice?" asked Reg quietly.

"If that's what you want," replied Terry looking surprised.

"No, it's not what I want," answered Reg firmly. "I want to open on Boxing night."

"Then you'll need someone else," replied Terry straightening up and looking Reg in the eye. "I don't want to leave, but I will. You can have my notice. I'll pack my things and go now."

"Okay," paused Reg. "If that's what you want to do." Reg was disappointed he had called Terry's bluff and lost, not only a good friend but also a good manager.

As 1959 came to an end, Reg considered his failures, and focused on success. He was ready to start a new year with more ideas and schemes to try. Dorothy packed to go to Huddersfield leaving Reg on his own. Her year had been ups and downs, with more downs than ups and she was still living in Portland Terrace!

Photo:
Reg Calvert with
Baby Bubbly.
*(Watching):*
Dave Da Costa,
Danny Storm,
Ricky Fever,
Glen Dale.

## NOTES: EQUALITY AND THE WIND OF CHANGE

*1959 General Election, Harold Macmillan led the Conservative party to victory. On his visit to Cape Town, he made it clear he was opposed to segregation and gave a speech where he spoke of the "wind of change" blowing through Africa. He aimed to create a society that respected the right of individuals and, controversially, suggested majority black populations in British colonies could claim the right to rule themselves.*

*The 1960's promised a more enlightened society with opportunities and freedoms not experienced by previous generations. Immigration increased and the pressure on jobs and housing was severe. It was not uncommon to see signs displayed in boarding houses and at factory gates saying 'No Blacks,' and sometimes 'No Blacks or Irish.'*

*Only 32 years earlier, in 1928, women were given the right to vote. This did not make them equal, and they were in many ways, treated as second-class citizens. A woman earned approximately half the wage of a man doing the same job and there was little opportunity for promotion. Few women were financially independent and it was unheard of for a woman to obtain a mortgage or sign a hire purchase agreement without a male guarantor.*

*On 8th November 1960, John F. Kennedy was elected President of the U.S.A. The American struggle for human rights, equality and non-segregation caused frequent "race riots." Black men were called 'boys' by their white 'superiors' and to counteract this, young men, whatever creed or colour, included 'man' into the conversation. 'Man' became the 'in' word.*

## 1960 MUSIC TRENDS

The British music scene was in the ascendance and the Americans were moving over but not out. Cliff Richard topped the charts with: "Please Don't Tease", "Voice in the Wilderness", "Fall in Love With You" and "Nine Times out of Ten." His backing group, The Shadows, had a hit with: "Apache". Adam Faith: "Poor Me," "What Do You Want?" "Made You," "Someone Else's Baby." "How About That" and "When Johnny Comes Marching Home."

Reg booked top recording stars including: Billy Fury who had a hit with "Collette." Tommy Bruce & The Bruisers: "Ain't Misbehavin." Johnny Kidd & The Pirates: "Shakin' All Over." Emile Ford: "What Do you Want to Make Those Eyes At Me For?" and "On A Slow Boat To China."

Other Brits to make the charts included Anthony Newley with "Why," "Do You Mind" and "If She Should Come To You." Shirley Bassey: "As Long As He Needs Me." Lonnie Donegan: "My Old Man's A Dustman", and "I Wanna Go Home." Acker Bilk and his Paramount Jazz Band: "Summer Set." Tommy Steele, now a film star, with: "Little White Bull". Comedian, Max Bygraves: "Fings Ain't Wot they Used T Be" and Comedian, Ken Dodd: "Love Is Like A Violin."

From America, the Everly Brothers topped the charts with: "Cathy's Clown", "When Will I Be Loved", "Lucille", and "So Sad". Elvis with: "Mess of Blues", "It's Now or Never" and "Stuck on You". Roy Orbison: "Only The Lonely". "Jimmy Jones: "Handy Man" and "Good Timin." Johnny Preston: "Cradle of Love." Jim Reeves: "He'll Have to Go." Neil Sedaka: "Oh Carol" and "Stairway to Heaven."

April 1960, Gene Vincent toured England with a little known American singer, Eddie Cochran. Buddy Holly had died the previous year in an air crash and Eddie, having a premonition, was reluctant to do the tour but had been persuaded. Travelling in a taxi in Wiltshire, the vehicle lost control. As the car went into a skid, Eddie, seated in the centre of the back seat, threw himself over his fiancé to save her. The passenger door flew open and he was flung out of the car and died later of head injuries. Gene Vincent suffered severe leg injuries.

Eddie Cochran had written a song with his brother and recorded it with Buddy Holly's backing group, The Crickets. The record company immediately released the song, "Three Steps To Heaven," which became a poignant, posthumous hit.

# 14. THE NAMING GAME

Vince Taylor's tour of the dance halls came to an end in January 1960 and he was offered work in France. Reg had paid the Playboys while they had been on tour for him but now they were thinking of travelling to France with Vince. There was one new recruit Reg had been watching and wanted to retain.

"Have you decided what you want to do next?"

"I thought I'd go to France," replied Geoffrey Glover-Wright.

"Not a good idea," said Reg, conspiratorially.

"Why not?"

"Vince is not, how should I say this, a very stable character. Who will pay your wages?"

"Vince said he'd pay me," replied Geoffrey confidently. "The other guys are all sticking with him."

"Have you thought about becoming a singer?" asked Reg tentatively.

"Not really."

"If you joined us you could have your own backing group," tempted Reg.

Geoffrey smiled in reply.

"There's a job here, working for me, with free accommodation and a regular weekly wage. You'll earn more money and be featured on the shows," said Reg, as he paused and felt in his pocket for a packet of cigarettes. He opened the packet and offered one to Geoffrey. Reg sparked the lighter and held the flame up. Geoffrey inhaled smoke and nicotine until the end of the cigarette glowed red. Slowly removing the cigarette and holding it between his fingers they both watched the small spiral of smoke drift upwards. The decision was made.

"I don't like to let Vince down," replied Geoffrey, conscientiously.

"He'll be okay," smiled Reg. "Do you think you could do some Buddy Holly numbers if I get the records?"

"I expect so," replied Geoffrey, hesitating.

"Good," said Reg. "We'll need to give you a stage name."

"A stage name?" queried Geoffrey, smiling at the prospect.

"Everyone has a stage name," replied Reg, returning his smile.

"Okay. What do you think?"

"If you wore dark horn rimmed glasses like Buddy Holly you would stand out. And we could call you Buddy."

"Buddy Glover-Wright?" suggested Geoffrey.

"No, that's a bit formal. We need something catchy. Something that people will remember."

The "naming" game was now well established with the boys. They collected together in the office and with much laughter, some deliberation and discussion, a name was decided upon. Dressed in a black suit, horn rimmed glasses and high heeled Cuban cowboy boots, "Buddy Britten" stood out in a crowd. He was strikingly different to Danny Storm or any of the other singers and his backing group were named the "Regents."

Buddy moved into the Bandbox and several weeks later was surprised when Doris, his glamorous German girlfriend arrived unannounced. She had decided to move from London to stay with him, bringing with her an enormous amount of luggage. Buddy made his mark and became a dance hall 'star,' expanding his repertoire by singing some Buddy Holly numbers and playing rhythm and blues, which appealed to the boys in the audience.

Playboys, Brian Marshall, Johnny Vance and Johnny Watson went to France. Johnny Vance had got a girl in the "family" way and he was worried and not ready for marriage. Going to France was a means of escape. Several months later the Playboys returned to England penniless. For three months they took residency at the 2i's Coffee Bar, backing Vince and other singers, they were paid one pound a night each until Vince was offered work in the U.S.A. Without informing the Playboys, he left on a plane and "forgot" to pay their wages. Bass player, Johnny Vance and drummer, Johnny Watson, returned to Southampton and were pleased when Reg offered to employ them again.

During the year, some very good musicians and singers joined Reg including guitarist and singer Roy Phillips; pianist and singer, Roy Young; guitarist, Tony Harvey; pianist, Alan Le Clair; drummer, Bobby Woodman and bass guitarist, Heinz Burt. Heinz was recruited to play with the Strollers backing Danny Storm. To make him stand out, Reg suggested he dye his hair blond. Heinz was not so good at playing guitar or singing but he was striking with his blond hair and good looks and fitted in with the boys.

Don Ker and Martin Upperdine were waiting apprehensively in Coventry. When they received a telegram "Please meet me at Staines Town Hall, Monday evening," they were thrilled. They had made it into show business. Martin and Don packed their bags and went. In Coventry they earned three pounds a week and Reg started them off on five pounds plus an extra pound for Don as he was a qualified driver and could drive a van to the dance halls. After a short while their wages increased to eight pounds a week.

"We need to find you a stage name. We can't bill you as Martin Upperdine," said Reg looking closely at his new singer.
"I agree man," replied Martin. "Why don't we use my middle name and call me "Johnny Martin?"
"Sounds better, yes, I like it. Johnny Martin," agreed Reg.
"You could call me the "blond bombshell," Johnny suggested, conscious of his new dyed blond hairstyle.
"Great," agreed Reg. "I'll bill you as the "Big Beat Blond Bombshell."
"That's fantastic," said Johnny, who couldn't believe his luck.

Don and Martin were offered free accommodation in the end house of Portland Terrace. Dave Da Costa and Debbie had moved out to live on the top floor of the house in Derby Road. The weather was exceptionally cold and the house, with no electricity or heating was like living in an icebox. Mrs MacDonald heard about their plight from her daughter, Donna, who worked in the Bandbox shop and invited them to come and lodge at her house where they appreciated home comforts.

Reg's entourage grew with the addition of Freddy Weir and the Weir Wolves and he dressed them all in bright red satin shirts and black trousers. Freddy, dark skinned and strikingly good-looking originated from Sarawak in New Borneo; his act was unusual as he played a large white double bass and sang. The drummer, Ian

Anthonizs, born in Singapore, sometimes had a haunted look about him and it was rumoured he had accidentally killed his sister whilst playing in a sword fight.

Edward Bennett worked on the markets and looked almost exactly like Elvis Presley. Unfortunately, this Elvis could neither sing nor keep time, but Reg was unperturbed. Edward had the potential to be a dance hall star and Reg knew he would improve with training and rehearsal. The 'naming' was difficult. The boys all got together and shouted out different suggestions. Edward's first stage name was Eddie Thunder but with that name, girls in the audience took little notice. Reg changed his name to Eddie Sexman, with little affect. Finally he tried an outrageous name. One no one would forget. Eddie Sex, dressed in a gold satin jacket, sent the girls wild. With the cacophony of noise from screaming girls, guitars and drums, no one could hear Eddie sing or whether he was in time or not. A sensitive young man, conscious of his limitations and lack of ability, Eddie Sex rehearsed to improve. The other boys tried to help and Don Ker spent hours working over numbers. Gradually he did improve a little. Just because he could make the girl's scream was no reason for him to be complacent.

Clarence Fender was different, he was just fifteen and had recently left school, was small, baby faced and he was black. Everyone took an immediate liking to him.

"We'll need to give you a stage name my friend," said Reg.

"Okay man," replied Clarence, smiling broadly. Like many black people, he encountered prejudice nearly every day of his life but he was lucky. He found a manager who treated him as an equal with the white boys.

"Clarence Fender," pondered Reg. "Fender guitars."

"I don't play guitar man," said Clarence.

"You ought to learn," suggested Reg. "You remind me a bit of Cuddly Dudley and a bit like Little Richard.

"Yeah Man," agreed Clarence.

"What about Cuddly Fender?" suggested one of the boys.

Reg paused to think and repeated. "Cuddly Fender, no, that doesn't ring."

"How about Cuddly Bubbly?" came another suggestion.

"No man. I don't think that sounds good," replied Clarence.

"Cuddly, Bubbly, Hubble," suggested another, laughing at his joke.

"Clarence Star."

"Star Fender."

"Bubbly Fender."

Once again, the naming game was in full swing and everyone called out suggestions until the name was agreed.

"Baby Bubbly. That's it," said Reg.

"Okay man, I'll be Baby Bubbly," agreed Clarence, smiling broadly with his white teeth shining in his dark face. "I like that. Baby Bubbly."

Owen Jones, tall, slightly gangly and out of step with his body, contrasted to the good-looking Bandbox boys. Not that he was unattractive, he just wasn't good looking nor did he have 'sex' appeal. What he did possess was an excellent voice and he was quick to learn new songs. Naming Owen took a little longer. Reg wanted a stage name to make the girls interested. Eventually, Owen was re-named Ricky Fever.

Independence from home and being a "rock 'n' roll" musician came at a price. Appearance was important. The boys like young peacocks, thought sex and fashion had been invented just for them. They bought the latest fashions and time was spent grooming their hair, dying it blond or black, whichever was required for their stage persona. Smoking cigarettes and eating in cafés quickly absorbed increased wages. They stopped at regular transport cafés on their travels and the Kingsland Café, opposite the Bandbox was a favourite with dockers, seamen and the boys, providing inexpensive, greasy fry-ups such as sausages or Spam fritters, egg and chips.

Colin Angel and the Choir Boys knew Reg was paying his other new recruits five pounds a week and singers a lot more. They thought they would "push their luck" and ask for a pay rise. Together, they discussed a strategy and having all worked in industry, decided to take a gamble and go on strike. Secretly they agreed they would follow Reg for nothing just to be part of the scene, but at the same time they wanted equal pay.

"Come on boys," said Reg when he found them all idly sitting around and the van empty. "You should have left by now to do the West Country Tour."

"We're on strike," they replied looking sombre.

"On strike?" queried Reg, not quite believing what he had heard.

"We'd like more money," said Jeff Chalke, who became the spokesperson.

"Musicians don't go on strike," said Reg with a sense of humour. "You don't work in a factory or have a trade union."

"We want to be paid the same as the others," replied Jeff.

"You agreed on three pounds ten shillings a week and that is nearly double what you were earning before," responded Reg.

"We can't live on three pounds ten shillings a week. We need a rise or we're not working," said Jeff.

Reg took a deep breath and paused while he took a packet of cigarettes out of his pocket and handed them round. "You want more money?" said Reg as they all sat nonchalantly smoking. Reg realised he had no choice, the show had to go on. "Okay my friends, you win, I'll give you a rise to a fiver a week."

The Choir Boys cheered, they were in jubilant mood as they hastily packed the van ready for the tour. They were an integral part of the Danny Storm show with Johnny Watson on drums. The opening set saw Colin Angel singing, backed by the "Choir Boys." During the second set they backed a different singer who could be Eddie Sex, Dave Da Costa, Baby Bubbly, Johnny Martin, Carol Laine or a guest singer. For the third set the Choirboys morphed into the Strollers backing Danny Storm, the star of the show.

Johnny Martin thought he could save money by dying his own hair. His was naturally dark brown and when he saw his roots showing through, he bought a home colouring kit from the chemist in St Mary's and spent Sunday afternoon dyeing it. The instructions were simple but he didn't follow them. When he finished he dried his hair and looked at his reflection. To his dismay, he had turned his hair bright ginger. It was Sunday and tomorrow he was on the

West Country tour. In desperation, he returned to the same chemist and knocked on the door to the flat above.

"Sorry to trouble you," said Johnny politely. "Please can I buy another colouring kit? I can't go out tomorrow with ginger hair."

"I've only got a black kit left," frowned the chemist. "Do you want to go black?"

"It'll be better than ginger," said Johnny in dismay.

Monday morning dawned and none of the boys recognised Johnny and when Reg realised who he was, his annoyance was obvious. The posters were printed.

"We can hardly call you the blond bombshell now, my friend, can we?"

Touring was something to be endured if you wanted to be a 'star.' The boys joked about to pass the time and Johnny entertained everyone with his banter. He was a natural mimic and could take off most people he met. Reg heard him larking about and recognised his potential.

"Why don't you introduce comedy into your acts?" suggested Reg. "You could do a rock 'n' roll version of George Formby."

"No man," replied Johnny.

"You ought to try," encouraged Reg. "It would improve your act."

"I don't think it would be right for me to be funny on stage. It's not my image."

"You're a natural my friend. The girls will like you better if you can make them laugh," replied Reg wisely.

"No man, I want to be a sex idol not a comedian," replied Johnny. At nineteen he knew everything and he knew what he wanted to be. He wanted to be the 'Big Beat Blond Bombshell,' not a comic character.

The most unusual singer Reg employed to feature at the dance halls was David Sutch. He was his own manager and lived in north London with his mother. He methodically kept records so as not to repeat the same show at the same venue and gave himself the stage name of Screaming Lord Sutch. Unlike other singers, David made no effort to look handsome, growing unkempt black hair

129

unfashionably long, tied back in a ponytail. His horror acts were outrageous. Ear splitting screams, howling, and singing, combined with heavy rock as he appeared as Dracula, Jack the Ripper or a werewolf, sometimes emerging from a coffin. Girls watched mesmerised, screaming in terror whenever he leapt towards them with a real axe or knife.

When David Sutch was doing a tour of the dance halls, he stayed at the Bandbox and mixed in with the other boys. On one occasion, he asked Johnny Martin if he would like to help him choose a new suit and together, they went to a large department store where David headed for the soft furnishing department.

"What do you think of this material?" David asked.

"What for man?" asked Johnny.

"For my new suit."

"A suit! This is curtain material man. You can't make a suit out of curtain material."

"I like the pattern," replied David pulling out the roll.

Seeing the two young men showing an unusual interest in fabrics, a shop assistant came over and asked if she could help.

"Yes marm," replied David who was always more than polite. "Can you measure me for a suit?"

"We don't make suits here," replied the surprised assistant.

"Don't you?" asked David seriously, with a twinkle in his eye.

"You need the men's tailoring department, downstairs," replied the assistant.

"Do I?" replied David. "But it says you make to measure."

"Curtains sir," replied the assistant.

"But you could measure me for a suit," insisted David.

"I'll call the manager over," replied the assistant.

After some discussion, it was agreed that David could have a suit made in the gents department with the fabric he had selected.

Reg employed only one steward, a retired boxer to go to some of the dances, a large man who was a little punch drunk. If someone clinked the side of a glass he immediately stood up, as if he was in a boxing ring. Dance hall fights were uncommon and Reg sorted out troublemakers by stepping on stage and taking the microphone to request them to stop. If they continued fighting, he jumped down into the fray, picked up the offender and carried him outside to cool off. On some occasions he picked up two, one under each arm and carried them out and banged their heads together!

On stage, the boys flirted outrageously with the girls in the audience, ignoring testosterone-fired boyfriends who did not like the competition. While performing, there was an invisible dividing line that girls nor boys in the audience rarely crossed. When they were off stage it was a different matter, they became normal mortals and jealous boyfriends sometimes waited at the end of the dance to abuse them or pick a fight. The boys took care to stick together for protection while they were loading the van. After one show an angry young man made his way to Johnny Martin and held up a mirror and thrust it aggressively in Johnny's face.

"Have a look at that."

"Yes," replied Johnny, trying to push the mirror away.

"I'm going to cut your face up with this mirror later tonight."

"Please don't do that. I'm not the best-looking guy around and you don't want to take away what little I've got," replied Johnny with bravado.

The scene was related to Reg, who reassured him he would look out for him. Like a father figure, Reg kept a protective eye on his boys, always calm in difficult situations. Although he seemed easygoing and great fun to work for, he was one hundred percent professional when it came to putting on a show. When he was really angry it was obvious, his face would go ashen and his eyes turned cold steely grey. One glance from Reg was enough for that person to know they had stepped out of line. If one of his boys behaved badly, he would give them a stern talking to, or make his point by bringing his hand hard down on a table top to make a loud slapping sound.

Danny Storm had that rare quality of combining good looks with modesty and charm. He paid attention to what Reg said and rapidly improved his performance and attracted many female fans, and a small male following. After a while, he reverted his hair back to blond and no longer looked like Cliff Richard, but became "himself." Dave Jay took a particular interest in Danny's career and Mr Stennings, nicknamed 'Murial' by the boys, was also susceptible to his charms. Less welcome were jealous boyfriends who discovered where the boys lived and several times came to look for Danny at the Derby Road house.

On Friday mornings, the boys made their way to the office for their wages. Mr Stennings had the money prepared in little brown envelopes and as he handed them out, he would try to catch hold of Danny's hand and hold it for a moment. If he succeeded, it was a bonus. Mostly Danny laughed and teased him, snatching the small brown envelope and darting out of the office calling, "Catch me if you can."

Len Canham often propositioned Reg's boys and they found it extremely embarrassing. If they were waiting backstage in a narrow space, Len pressed his body against theirs as he passed. Reg shrugged the problem off as part of life and told the boys to ignore him. It was well known in the entertainment business for some impresarios and managers to have a partiality for young men. Some of the boys appealed to Dorothy as they were getting to the point of refusing to work at the Pier for Len.

"You'll have to speak to Len," said Dorothy.

"I can't," replied Reg. "What can I say?"

"I don't know. But something needs to be said. The boys are very edgy about working at the Pier. He's tried to get several to go to bed with him. It's one thing to be a homosexual and keep it to yourself but quite another to try and pervert young boys."

"It's too difficult," replied Reg.

"It's not fair on our boys. Some are only sixteen or seventeen. It's okay for him to get his fancy boy singers up from London but he has to know, he can't have our boys. You need to speak to him."

"Okay. I'll try," replied Reg.

For months, Dorothy kept reminding Reg to do something about it. Reluctantly, he opened the subject with Len, and the two men argued. Len was quite affronted to be accused.

"You have to understand that when you employ my boys you can't proposition them," said Reg quietly.

"I never proposition boys."

"That's not what my boys are telling me."

"If that's how you feel we don't need to do any further business. Get out," replied Len angrily.

"I'm sorry you feel like that," answered Reg, trying to make the peace.

"Get out," indicated Len pointing at the door.

Reg walked out and the two men discontinued their business relationship and a quiet war started as they competed against each other. After a few months, it settled down and they began to work tentatively together again, exchanging musicians without mentioning their argument.

*Photo (Above)*:
(?). Gene Vincent, Roy Young and Reg Calvert.

*(Top right)*:
Ian Anthoniz and Don Ker. (JM)

*(Bottom right)*:
Freddy Weir, Carol Laine. (JM)

# 15. NOT ANGELS OR CHOIR BOYS

The boys were not "angels" or "choir boys." They lived the life of rock 'n' roll "stars" and one of the perks of the job was meeting stage-struck girls who stood in small clusters, giggling and waiting for them to sign autographs. Some girls were more brazen and at the end of the dance, eyed up the boys as they loaded the vans and made it obvious they wanted more than an autograph. Few boys considered the consequences of their 'one night stands,' and never questioned the age of the girls. The only form of contraception they used was the risky method known by the colloquialism, 'Jumping off Edge Hill.'

Drugs were not generally available or used by many teenagers and there was no alcohol at the dances. Cannabis was smoked by a few of the London groups that toured and you could buy amphetamines such as Preludin and Benzedrine in a St Mary's shop. These had a euphoric and stimulant effect. Some of the boys experimented but didn't continue. Don Ker tried Benzedrine several times to keep him awake when he was on the West Country tour. Danny Storm and Colin Angel decided to try cannabis. They were both so ill it put them off trying anything else.

Away from their parents and Reg, the boys looked forward to a good time on the West Country tour. Several of the Choir Boys arranged a rendezvous with girls after a dance on a warm summer evening. Earlier they had bought Benzedrine Nasal Inhalers, broke the tube and swallowed the contents. It made their heads feel very large. They met the girls and instead of leading them astray and having a romantic evening, they sat in a church graveyard leaning on gravestones and talking. They talked and talked the whole night through about their revelation. They had just discovered the answer to life and the universe! One of boys took too much Benzedrine and was out all night on his own. Next morning they hunted for him and found him talking to a red post box. He thought it was a person.

The cost of "digs" while they were on tour was around ten shillings a night and the boys were given extra money to cover it. To encourage them to save, Reg suggested they buy their own sleeping bag and camp in the van or sleep in the back office of the Exeter dance hall. If they were lucky they often had a girl in the sleeping bag with them or went back to a girl's house to sleep on a settee.

Some journeys were more eventful than others. The Choir Boys, returning home from the West Country with Ricky Fever as the driver, stopped in the New Forest by the Rufus Stone so they could "relieve" themselves and break the journey. With no one else around, they started to play about and pulled the sign out of the ground and pretended to fight with it. They hit Ricky Fever on the head and he fell to the ground unconscious. They thought he was feigning injury but when he started to have an epileptic fit, they realised it was serious. They looked from one to the other with the realisation they were doomed to stay in the forest for the night. Ricky was the only person qualified to drive.

"I know how to drive my father's car," said Jeff Chalke with bravado. "I've driven it in the garage."

The boys looked at him, he was their only chance and they nodded agreement. Ricky was shoved into the back of the van and Jeff started the engine. He drove very slowly, in first gear, all the way back to Southampton and parked in Portland Terrace, where they guiltily alighted and made their own way home.

Cliff Bennett and the Rebel Rousers were booked to do a West Country tour and after only two days away, Dorothy received an early morning telephone call with the news that there was a serious problem and the tour could not go on. She immediately ran upstairs and woke Reg who was asleep after a late night.

"Would you believe it?" she said as she shook him. "The show will have to be cancelled. The boys are in trouble with the police."

"You're joking?" said Reg blearily, sitting up in bed and getting a cigarette out of the packet. "What have they done?"

"Something really, really stupid," replied Dorothy. "They've been pinching sixpences out of milk slot machines."

A grin spread across Reg's face. "You're joking? They wouldn't do that."

"That's what the police said and they've got them locked up. I'm sure Cliff has put them up to it."

"He's a bit of a lad," agreed Reg.

"You'll have to go down and sort them out," replied Dorothy. "They're supposed to be playing tonight."

"I can't," said Reg. "I've too many things on today and speakers to repair for tonight. Can you go and sort it out and try and put a show together?"

"Damn," said Dorothy looking at her watch. "I've got a big print order to do."

"Can't you "phone the customer and make some excuse and let them have it tomorrow?"

"I suppose I'll have to," replied Dorothy crossly as she started to pack a few things into a travel bag.

"Let's have a kiss," said Reg, grabbing her hand.

"No, I don't feel like it," replied Dorothy pulling away.

"I always love you when you're cross."

"I know you do," said Dorothy with a wry smile. "I'll leave a note out for Susan to cook a meal and feed the animals. It never rains but it pours."

As Dorothy was leaving, Johnny Martin strolled over.

"What's the matter Mrs C?"

"Cliff Bennett," replied Dorothy biting her lip.

"Isn't he on the West Country tour?" asked Johnny.

"Yes, that's where I'm going. They're in big trouble," replied Dorothy curtly.

"Do you want me to come and keep you company? I'm not working today."

Dorothy smiled warmly. "Yes, it would be good to have some company." In the van she related the problem to Johnny. "It's not funny," said Dorothy when she saw out of the corner of her eye he was grinning.

"No, it isn't," replied Johnny, trying to be straight faced.

"Cliff's a bad influence but our boys should know better."

A few hours later Dorothy arrived in Exeter. She met the downcast boys at the police station and did her best to pour oil on troubled waters. Dorothy appeared in court on behalf of the boys and fortunately the Magistrate was generous. It was their first offence and they were released on a caution.

Rory Blackwell, unemployed after his stint at Butlins, was looking for work and Reg invited him to come and do a tour of the dance halls and help run the Bandbox. Rory, five years younger than Reg was still "rocking." He accepted the offer and moved in to the ground floor flat behind the club with his wife and baby daughter. To promote both Rory and the club, Reg suggested he should think about trying to beat the Guinness World Record for drumming. There was already some rivalry between drummer Ray Du Val and Rory, both trying to beat each other on different occasions. Rory took up the challenge and the event was staged at the Bandbox where visitors were welcome to come and watch the event. After two days of drumming, first one hand then the other, then one foot and then the other, Rory was flagging and ready to sleep.

"Only two more days to go," said Reg cheerfully.

"I don't know if I can make it," replied Rory.

"Of course you can," encouraged Reg. "I'll make some coffee."

"I need something stronger than coffee," replied Rory as he continued to drum while he closed is eyes.

"Don't go to sleep now," said Reg. "Open your eyes."

"I'm tired man," replied Rory as he continued to hit the drum.

Dave Jay kept a watch on Rory, helping to sustain him by bringing drinks to suck through a straw and feeding him sandwiches. When he needed the toilet, someone went with Rory and held a drum so he could play non-stop. Southern Television came to film the event for the "grand finale." Rory was near to collapse and there was a big countdown when he reached the former record of eighty-two hours and thirty-five minutes. Rory, almost delirious, managed to do a small drum roll to acknowledge his victory. He looked as though he would fall off the drum stool. Surely, he must stop playing? With every fibre and muscle in his body hurting, Rory continued drumming so the film crew went away. Eventually, Rory capitulated to the pain and exhaustion. After eighty-four hours of non-stop drumming and supported, one man each side, he stepped down from the rostrum and collapsed on the floor.

"Dave, quickly, "phone the film crew and get them back. Tell them Rory has done it," said Reg smiling broadly.

The film crew returned to find Rory unconscious on the floor. "Can you get him to play the drums again, so we can film him doing his final drum roll?" asked the camera crew as they stood by the sleeping man.

"I'll see what I can do," replied Dave as he started to shake Rory.

"Come on man, you have to do it for the television. Wake up man!" shouted Dave, lifting his head up. "Just a little more drumming and then you can go to bed."

With great difficulty, Dave managed to get Rory to his feet and up to the rostrum to hold the drum sticks and re-enact the finale of his drumming marathon. With the crowd cheering, Rory laid down his sticks for a second time. He had achieved his goal and made it onto television and into the 1960 Guinness Book of Records.

By the summer of 1960, Reg had four shows touring the dance halls but he was ambitious and hoped one day to have ten touring shows. He did not want the Choir Boys to go on strike again so he encouraged Jeff Chalke to learn bass guitar. Once he was proficient, Jeff was moved from the Choir Boys and joined Freddy Weir and the Weir Wolves.

*Photo:* 1959 Danny Storm, Colin Angel, Buddy Britten, Baby Bubbly, Pete Mist. Reg behind holding poster. (West Country tour). (JM)

Reg took turns to go on the various tours to ensure all the dances were being well run and the dance hall figures remained high. His eyesight was bad and he preferred to be driven rather than drive himself. When they travelled down to the West Country, to relieve the long journey and the monotony of travel, Reg developed a new sport. A glass lemonade bottle was saved and thrown out of the window at a pretty bridge they regularly passed. Reg threw it most weeks, and everyone cheered as it hit the corner and smashed into little pieces. One week, Jeff Chalk took up the challenge. Jeff took aim and hit the bridge perfectly but the bottle did not smash. It bounced back at him like a boomerang and with a loud crashing sound, shattered the side windscreen.

"That was stupid," said Reg crossly. "You'll have to pay for a new windscreen out of your wages. I'll tell Mr Stennings to dock it."

"But you told me to do it," stammered Jeff in surprise.

"You don't have to do everything I tell you," retorted Reg irritably.

Nothing else was said about the window and Jeff was pleased to see that he had a full wage packet at the end of the week.

Occasionally, Dorothy did the West Country tour with the boys. She felt confident enough to leave Susan, now aged twelve, to take care of her younger sister, their pets and to cook the evening meals with Reg returning home for the meal before leaving again to run the dances. The boys were not keen on Dorothy travelling with them, she was stricter than Reg and they had to behave. Benzedrine, girls in sleeping bags and throwing bottles at bridges was not mentioned or even considered when Dorothy was with them. She encouraged them to do more sophisticated things to pass the time, like taking them to Paignton Zoo.

During the summer, Dorothy's mother came to stay and Dorothy planned a holiday in the West Country, combining work with pleasure and she also invited Mrs Maslin with her family to join them. The weather was sunny and blustery and they enjoyed all the typical seaside holiday activities, picnicking on the beach, playing ball, crazy golf and going to Paignton Zoo. More exciting for Susan and Candy were the few days away with their father when the dance halls were closed for the summer break. Reg took them camping with some local children who wanted to come, and packed his car with cardboard boxes, blankets, pillows, tins of food and camping things. He drove to a deserted sand quarry near the New Forest, the perfect place to have a weekend camp, away from civilisation. The children slept in a cardboard box each with a blanket and Reg slept on the back seat of the car. They were allowed to be wild children to roam free, climb trees and were encouraged to be "daredevils" and jump off cliffs into the soft sand below. In the evening, they sat around a camp-fire singing while Reg cooked sausages and baked beans. Afterwards, with lumps of clay he had collected, Reg showed them how to make thumb pots and heat them in the hot ashes of the fire to make them hard.

Odd things started to happen in the autumn of 1960 that puzzled Dorothy. Items went missing from their home. The children's post office savings books, her new underwear and other small items. Travelling back from the Bandbox one Saturday afternoon, she slowed at a crossroads, put her foot on the brake and could not find the pedal. The vehicle kept moving. She drove across a busy junction with vehicles blaring their horns as they swerved to miss her. Shocked, she brought the van to a halt by using her gears.

"We think your brake wire was cut," explained a mechanic.

"Cut?" queried Dorothy. "You mean cut with a knife or something?"

"We think so," replied the mechanic. "It's a clean cut. Not a fray."

"Vandalism," asked Dorothy.

"Most yobs don't vandalise brakes," replied the mechanic. "They pinch cars and go for a joy ride until the petrol runs out."

"I was lucky then," replied Dorothy, wondering who would want to cut her brake wire and whether someone was trying to kill or injure her.

As Reg earned more money, he increased the wages of his singers and musicians. Some dance halls flourished while others closed after a few weeks. For the first time in British history, thousands and thousands of teenagers across the south and central England were provided with entertainment designed especially for them.

## DANCE HALLS BOOKED AT:

Andover, Bournemouth, Bishops Waltham, Broughton, Camberley, Cheltenham, Christchurch, Eastleigh, Evesham, Exeter, Exmouth, Fareham, Farnham, Fordingbridge, Torquay, Guildford, Hackney, High Wycombe, Islington, Kettering, Kings Somborne, Longton, Lye, Lymington, Ludgershall, Melksham, Newbury, Portsmouth, Rochester, Romsey, Salisbury, Staines, Southsea, Stockbridge, Swindon, Toton, Trowbridge, Torquay, Weymouth, Winchester and Worcester.

***** 

Dave Jay was sent further north to explore potential new dance halls as Reg wanted to expand his empire. Dave could not drive so travelled by train and bus and reported back to Reg each day by telephone. It was relatively expensive to make calls from a public 'phone box so Dave rang the office and shouted down the receiver the number of the telephone box and Reg called him back.

New venues were booked at Derby, Peterborough, Birmingham, West Bromwich, Stourbridge, Tamworth, Nuneaton, Rugby, Warwick and Wisbeach. Finding accommodation for the boys while they were on the "northern" tour was difficult. Most hotels and guest-houses refused to have noisy pop stars staying in their establishment, as they would disturb other guests.

The Seven Stars, a quaint Victorian public house in Rugby was different and welcomed the boys and the landlord did not complain at the noise. The rooms had double beds and the boys had to share but this was preferable to sleeping bags on the floor.

Ghosts, imagined or real, haunted their rooms and the landlady confirmed other guests had seen ghosts. Several boys reported seeing ghostly apparitions and Buddy Britten was terrified as he was woken by something invisible pressing down hard on his chest. When the lights went out, even more ghosts appeared as the boys larked about and dressed up in sheets and pretended to be ghosts. Danny Storm climbed in the wardrobe and hid so he could jump out and frighten everyone. Instead, he came out, as white as a sheet after experiencing "something" in the wardrobe with him!

# 16. SCHOOL OF ROCK 'N' ROLL

Despite illness, the show had to go on. If the boys were ill, Reg still expected them to work whatever was wrong with them. When Don Ker became ill he refused to go on the West Country tour.

"I can't go Reg," said Don in a gruff voice, blowing his nose. "I feel too bad."

"You have to," said Reg. "We have a show and there's no one to replace you."

"You shouldn't make him go," said Johnny Martin sticking up for his friend.

"I can see he has a cold but I can't help that. He has to go," insisted Reg. "The drummer has chickenpox and he's still on tour."

"I can't Reg," insisted Don, shivering. "I feel too ill."

"You have a choice. You can go or stay behind. But if you stay behind you can look for another job," said Reg looking directly into Don's bloodshot eyes.

"If he goes, I go," said Johnny defiantly.

"That's up to you my friend," said Reg coolly. "You both have free choice."

"You go on the tour without me. There's no need for you to lose your job," said Don as he coughed and sneezed. "I'm going back to bed."

Don Ker left Reg's employment but good musicians can always find work and several months later he was employed by Len Canham. When Johnny returned from the tour he started to come out in spots. He had caught chicken pox from Tony Burnett.

"I can't go on the stage like this," he said to Reg. "I look awful covered in spots."

"That's up to you Johnny," replied Reg looking at him.

"I think I'd better go home to Coventry until I'm better," said Johnny.

"Okay my friend," replied Reg, looking at him sideways. "If that's what you want to do."

The newspapers were beginning to take notice of the man who was running so many teenage dances and employing a stable of pop groups. They were often featured in the local press but not all of what they wrote was complimentary.

The Camberley newspaper had several times written favourably about the Thursday night rock 'n' roll dances at the Agincourt but when they reproduced a large photograph of Eddie Sex, looking much like Elvis, Eddie was so upset, he lost his confidence to continue. The editorial headline slated the dance hall star for his lack of ability to sing in tune.

"How's this for a stupid, sickening bit of ballyhoo. A Barrow boy called Bennett changed his name to Mr. Sex,"

After Eddie had read the article, he went to find Reg in the Bandbox office.

"I think it's time for me to go back home," said Eddie disconsolately, holding the newspaper.

"You're fine," replied Reg as he sat at his desk, working out the next three weeks programme of shows. "Take no notice. It makes your name and the girls love you. You put on a good show and that's what it's all about."

"I do my best and it's been great. But I'm no good at learning my songs," replied Eddie. "The paper's right."

"Don't take it to heart my friend," replied Reg cheerfully. "All news is good news whatever they say."

"I've thought it through. I'll stay to finish the tour so you can find someone else."

"Don't rush into leaving. See how you feel next week and if you still feel the same I'll get a replacement," replied Reg amiably. "What do you plan to do if you leave?"

"Probably go back to the markets," replied Eddie.

"Well I hope you re-consider," said Reg. "Take good and bad publicity in your stride."

"Thanks Reg, but I've made up my mind to go home," replied Eddie more cheerfully when he realised Reg was not displeased with the article.

Reg nodded his acceptance and offered Eddie a cigarette. "If that's your decision, I'll look around for another singer."

The promoter, Don Arden, booked Gene Vincent to do a tour of Reg's dance halls in the autumn of 1960. He was a big star attraction, more popular in England than the U.S.A. perhaps in part, due to the publicity around the tragic accident with Eddie Cochran. To keep the costs low, and the ticket price affordable, Reg's musicians had to learn how to back the stars and expand their repertoire. In addition, on a 'famous star' night, local groups volunteered to perform for nothing, just to get their name on the same bill and most of them liked to return to the Bandbox and stay the night.

Gene was advertised to appear at the Rochester dance and when he did not arrive on time Reg became nervous. He paced about looking at his watch. Gene was beginning to get a bad reputation for being unreliable and there was no way to contact him to discover why he was late, or whether he would turn up. In desperation Reg decided to run a talent competition to fill in time.

"Good evening ladies and gentlemen, girls and boys. Tonight is your lucky night. We're having a talent competition. You could win five pounds if you get the most cheers." Reg in full swing, took over the stage, talking to the audience and firing their enthusiasm. "Come on. It's open to anyone. You there," said Reg, pointing to a girl in the audience, "Would you like to come up and sing for us?" The girl shook her head and her friends all pushed her. "Come on," said Reg. "Don't be shy."

Within a short time, various would-be stars took their turn to sing a number. The worse they were the louder the audience laughed and cheered.

"And your name is?" asked Reg as he gave the microphone to a good-looking young man with a mop of blond hair.

"Richard Scarforth."

"How old are you?"

"Twenty one."

"And what do you do for a living?"

"I work for British Rail as an engineer," replied Richard.

"And where do you come from?"

"Ashford. A friend of mine organised a coach trip to bring us here tonight,"

"So there's a few of you here from Ashford, let's have a cheer if you've caught the coach from Ashford." Reg waited for the cheering to finish. "And what song would you like to sing?"

"An Everly's number, All I have to do is dream."

Reg looked at the band for their approval to make sure they knew how to play it and they nodded. "Let's take it away for Richard."

Gene arrived and with relief Reg began to conclude the talent competition. "Let's have all the contestants back on stage. That's it, form a line. Now ladies and gentlemen, girls and boys, please give a cheer for your favourite singer. The one with the loudest cheer will be the winner."

Richard won the competition. There was no doubt as the crowd kept cheering. Reg held up the five-pound note and waved it about as he gave it to Richard and then escorted him to the side of the stage. "Have you ever thought about taking up singing

145

professionally?" asked Reg as he pulled the curtain cords and put a record on.

"Sorry we're late Reg," said Vince in his American drawl. "The van broke down and we had to fix it."

"Okay," replied Reg irritably. "Better late than never." Then looking back at Richard, he waited for his response.

"I was in a band called Dickie Lee and the Travellers," said Richard. "And we appeared on Southern Television on the Home Grown Show."

"That's fantastic," replied Reg. "So why haven't you taken it up professionally? Surely someone must have spotted you?"

"I don't know," replied Richard evasively. "I've just completed my apprenticeship."

Richard remembered the "Home Grown Show," and how, after his appearance, the producer had congratulated him. "You've got an exceptional voice and good looks to go with it. I'd like to make you into a star with lots more television appearances, would you like that?" Richard agreed he would like to be a star until he heard the terms. "Have you ever been to bed with a man before? I'm thinking of organising a little party with a few of my friends, if you get my drift? Come and have some fun with us." Richard, shocked by the suggestion, declined. The producer pointed out his terms. "It's up to you. You can be a star the easy way or do it the hard slog way."

"I'll do it the hard slog way," replied Richard, walking away in disgust.

"Would you like to come and work for me?" asked Reg. "Our base is in Southampton and I need a singer immediately. Can you start straight away?"

"You mean immediately, like tomorrow?" asked Richard, thinking quickly and wondering whether he could trust this man, give up a good job, and follow him?

"Yes. You can come with me tonight, after the show. I'll give you free accommodation. We have several houses in Southampton or you can find your own lodgings," continued Reg.

"I'll need to tell my parents and pack some things," replied Richard thoughtfully.

"I'll take you home after the show my friend," said Reg smiling warmly at his new recruit. "Meet me by the stage door at ten thirty."

Richard's parents were asleep so he woke them by turning the light on. "I've been offered a job," he said as they lay half asleep. "The man who runs the dance at Rochester needs a singer. He runs dance halls all over the country and he's offered me twenty pounds a week."

"Twenty pounds a week," repeated his amazed mother. What's his name?"

"Reg Calvert. I'll be based in Southampton."

"Is this what you want to do?" asked his father.

"Yes," replied Richard.

"You're sure?"

"Quite sure," replied Richard smiling.

"It's a bit of a risk," cautioned his father. "But you've a good voice and if it's what you want to do, you better get going."

Richard set off on his new life with Reg and travelled to Southampton and spent his first night at the Bandbox with most of the groups and singers from the Gene Vincent show. They slept anywhere, on camp beds, in sleeping bags or on the floor, wrapped in ex Army and Navy blankets. The following morning Reg arrived early and surprised everyone by making breakfast, a large pan of porridge to his own recipe, adding cream, butter and honey.

The 'naming' ceremony took place the next day for the new recruit, and after some discussion, Buddy Britten won the pound. Richard's new name was agreed. Glen Dale.

When Johnny Martin recovered from chicken pox, he telephoned Reg from Coventry to tell him the good news.

"I'm sorry Johnny. I've taken on another singer to replace you," said Reg.

"You can't have," said Johnny dismayed. "I've only been away two weeks."

"Sorry," apologised Reg. "I have to have a full show but if I have work any time, I'll contact you."

Johnny, flabbergasted and disappointed, reflected on his demise and realised he had crossed Reg several times. Worse still, he had not listened to advice nor developed his act and become versatile. But it was too late; he had had his opportunity and lost it.

Reg continued to look around for new challenges and things to do. He thrived on taking a gamble and became totally absorbed in each new venture. Other managers did not run dances and most recording stars were not rich as the amount of royalties they earned from selling records was minimal unless they wrote their own material. The only way they could earn a good income was by being on tour and even then, their managers took a big cut of their earnings. Larry Parnes and Don Arden organised big touring shows every few months as a way of promoting their protégés and paying their wages.

"What do you think about me organising a big show in a theatre somewhere?" asked Reg as he stirred the sugar round and round in the sugar bowl.

"You mean like the Cliff Richard show at the Gaumont?" asked Dorothy.

"That sort of thing."

"Not sure," replied Dorothy. "You'd need a big name."

"Hmm. I thought about Johnny Kidd and maybe Billy Fury or maybe that new singer, Ricky Valence."

"I like his song," replied Dorothy as she started to sing, with Reg joining in. *Tell Laura I Love Her, tell Laura I need her, tell Laura I might be late, I've something to do that cannot wait."*

"I think he'd be more of an attraction than Billy Fury," agreed Dorothy.

"Can you believe the BBC banned his record? I think he's managed by Norrie Paramour, the same chap who manages Cliff Richard."

"When were you thinking?" asked Dorothy.

"Mid October, probably Portsmouth Town Hall."

"Sounds okay, have you enough money saved for the up-front costs?"

"Should have," replied Reg, lighting another cigarette.

"Let's have a look at the costs and see whether it's feasible?" said Dorothy, picking up a notepad and pen. "How much will the town hall be?"

148

"Don't know," replied Reg, standing up. "I'll make some enquiries

"Okay," smiled Dorothy, pleased that Reg was going to be reasonable and make proper plans instead of doing everything in his head or on the inside of a cigarette packet.

The Portsmouth Town Hall was booked and tickets sold out. The boys were all excited to be part of their first 'big' show. The audience clapped with the music, some danced in the aisles and girls screamed at Danny Storm and the other boys. Backstage there were angry words, Johnny Kidd was furious with Ricky Fever as he had sung "Please Don't Touch," a number Johnny had planned to sing.

Ricky Valence, the star of the evening, stepped onto the stage and the girls screamed. Then they stopped, Ricky stood motionless, like a dummy. He sang some uninteresting numbers with no expression and although he had a very good tenor voice, his lack of projection and stage persona bored the audience. Once he had sung "Tell Laura I Love Her," the audience as one stood up and walked out, showing their displeasure with only a few people remaining in their seats to see the end of the show. What should have been a grand finale to a fantastic show, had in Reg's eyes, ended in failure. Deflated and disappointed he complained to Dorothy on their journey home. "It shouldn't be allowed, such a shame. It's not right for a manager to promote a young boy and make him a star without him first doing an apprenticeship. Boys have to learn how to perform to an audience."

Billy Fury, a rising star, was booked to tour the dance halls starting at the Bournemouth dance. He had no transport so Reg went to London with Carol Laine and brought him back to the Bandbox to travel with the boys.

"How was Billy Fury, did he put on a good show?" enquired Reg as Dorothy returned and entered the dining room door with her daughters laughing and chattering.

"Danny has a lot more about him," replied Dorothy going into the kitchen to put the kettle on.

"He wasn't that good," agreed Susan, who had watched him from the side of the stage.

"Who asked for your opinion?" joked Dorothy, smiling. "Now bed you two. It's late."

"What did the crowd think?" asked Reg.

"Billy has a good voice and he sings well but he just stood there. No charisma. No interaction with the crowd. A few stupid girls were screaming and tried to pull him into the audience."

"What did you do?" asked Reg.

"Got on the stage and pulled the girls off," laughed Dorothy.

No longer restrained by post war austerity, Reg was on the fast track to success. The culmination of four years hard work was bringing its rewards and he had earned respect by training his 'boys' to a high standard of professionalism and by treating them fairly and honestly. The only person he seemed not to treat fairly was Dorothy.

"It's time we thought about moving," said Dorothy, passing Reg a cup of coffee.

"I'm a bit busy at the moment," replied Reg.

"You're always busy. You never have time for me, or the girls and I'm fed up Reg. Really fed up. We need to move to a better house."

"I'm fed up with you nagging," replied Reg quietly as he looked at her coldly with steely grey eyes.

"I'm not nagging," shouted Dorothy, her temper flaring. "You promised." Dorothy knew Reg well enough to know when to stop and retreated to the kitchen, clanging plates and dishes about as she did the washing up. She needed to do something to shock Reg into considering her, but what?

Dorothy was often irritable and living with constant back pain made her even more irritable. Doctor Busk advised her to take it easy as her spine would continue to degenerate. He forecast that by the age of forty, she would be in a wheelchair if she did not look after herself. To help, he prescribed painkillers.

Most Saturday afternoons, Dorothy took her girls shopping, jostling with the crowds to look at all the wonderful displays of fashions and household items. Her mantra was, "You can look but don't touch." Rarely did she buy anything but after several hours, she treated herself and daughters to afternoon tea and cakes and when the waitress was not looking, they all sucked sugar cubes out of the bowl on the table.

The week Dorothy took the painkillers, she was happy and relaxed and took her daughters shopping as usual but to their surprise, and her own, she bought them all a new outfit. Laughing and smiling they returned home with their parcels.

"I like it when you take those tablets," remarked Susan.

"Why?" asked Dorothy.

"Because you don't shout any more," replied Susan, smiling happily as her mother put her arm about her affectionately.

"I'm sure it's these painkillers I'm on," said Dorothy.

"Why do you take them?"

"Because my back hurts so much," replied Dorothy. "It feels a lot better now but I'm sure it's not good to take painkillers. I think you can get addicted to them so I won't take them for long." After two weeks, Dorothy came off the painkillers and returned to her normal short-tempered self.

Dorothy decided she did not like the piano teacher Reg had chosen even though the girls were enjoying their lessons and making good progress. Susan loved classical music and he had sparked her enthusiasm by playing music by Beethoven, Handel and Bach to her and she progressed, little by little, through most of the Moonlight Sonata. Candy, more interested in pop music and less interested in the classics was still on easy pieces. Dorothy entered both girls into the Southampton Music Festival, in an age group two years older than their age, and warned her daughters, "You have to get at least eighty percentage marks or I will stop your lessons." The pieces of music were not inspiring and the girls did not practice them sufficiently.

"I'm stopping the girl's piano lessons," Dorothy informed Reg over breakfast.

"Why?" asked Reg.

"I told you before but you weren't listening. I told the girls that they had to get eighty percent or I would stop their lessons."

"We're a musical family," said Reg. "The girls should continue to learn."

"You might be from a musical family but I'm not. I live in the real world. That piano teacher is obviously no good or they would have got the marks."

"Susan seems to be doing well. She practices all the time," replied Reg looking hard at his wife.

"And Candy does," replied Dorothy defensively. "But they didn't practice the festival pieces and I warned them."

"That's very unfair," replied Reg angrily.

"What do you care? You're never here to help them. And you never leave the money for their lessons," replied Dorothy triumphantly.

"I don't agree with you. You should let them continue. He's a very good teacher," replied Reg.

"I don't think he is, he never does any theory with them and I'm not like you. I never go back on my word. When I say no, I mean no and the girls understand that," answered Dorothy. The conversation was over, she got up and walked out of the room, pleased that for once, she had shocked him.

Autumn changed to winter and misty mornings were blown away by chill, salty winds that came in off the sea. Travelling in the rear of the vans in the freezing weather was not a pleasure. The boys endured journeys, sitting uncomfortably on the floor on old cinema seats. When it was very cold, they placed a paraffin stove in the back of the van to keep them warm! Driving late at night down narrow lanes on icy roads was hazardous. The vans were frequently stopped by police patrols and waved on when the rear doors were opened and torch lights revealed a hoard of guitars, drum kit and sleepy boys.

Reg organised what had now become an annual event to be looked forward to, a bonfire night party, bigger and better than the previous year. He liked to have fun, but he was not happy. Leading a double life, he needed to make important decisions. Dorothy sensed his unease as he became more indifferent toward her. She planned her journey back to Huddersfield and wondered whether she ought to admit her marriage was a failure, and start again.

Not long after the bonfire party, Dorothy was quietly working in the typesetting room when Reg came rushing in, whistling, *All I have to do is dream*. He was in a good mood and as he entered the room, he put his arms around her, hugged her and lifted her feet off the floor.

"Put me down," squealed Dorothy, laughing.

"I've some news for you. Guess what it is?"

"No idea, you've seen a house to buy?"

"No. Guess again," grinned Reg, passing Dorothy a cigarette.

"I can't think, tell me," smiled Dorothy, happy that Reg was happy.

"Southern Television are going to do a show about the boys," replied Reg. "They telephoned the office this morning and asked if they could film us. Isn't that fantastic?"

"I can't believe it," beamed Dorothy. "When?"

"After Christmas, in mid January."

"That's brilliant. Fame at last," said Dorothy catching his enthusiasm. "You've worked hard enough for it."

"I'm going to book Eastleigh Town Hall for the filming. We've got to set everything up and rehearse. I've told the boys and they're really excited."

"I bet they are," replied Dorothy, wondering whether this could be the turning point, the start of a new direction for them both now that Reg had found success and was being recognised for the work he had done in leading the teenage entertainment boom?

"What's for dinner?" asked Reg.

"Ox heart casserole in orange sauce, for a change."

"That's different, I can smell it," replied Reg, trying not to turn up his nose. "Let's go out. The cat can eat the heart. I feel like celebrating. We can go to the Chinese restaurant in St Mary's."

"Okay, I'll tell the girls to get changed into their best dresses," said Dorothy, putting her tools neatly away. "They like the Chinese restaurant."

"Guess what they're going to call the film?" asked Reg smiling happily.

"Don't know?"

"Guess?"

"No idea. Tell me," laughed Dorothy.

**"The School of Rock 'n' Roll."**

*Photo:*
Baby Bubbly
with the
Choir Boys:
Pete Mist,
Dave Da Costa,
Colin Angel,
(Tony Burnett on
drums).

*Photo (below L- R. Front): 1960.* Dowland Brothers, Eddie Sex, Lucky Nelson, Danny Storm, Dorothy Calvert, Rory Blackwell, Dave Da Costa, Colin Angel, Carol Laine. *(Back):* Nevitt Brothers, (?), Pete Mist, Buddy Britten, Jeff Chalke, Tony Burnett. *(seated):* Reg Calvert.

# THE END IS JUST THE BEGINNING

**FILLONGLEY PUBLICATIONS,**
Fillongley, Warwickshire CV7 8PB
Book orders email:  fillongleypub@btinternet.com

154